PENGUIN BOOKS

THE MORALIST

Allen Wheelis is a psychoanalyst, essayist, philosopher, and novelist. In addition to *The Moralist*, he is the author of *The End of the Modern Age*, *The Illusionless Man: Some Fantasies and Meditations on Disillusionment*, *The Desert*, *The Quest for Identity*, and *The Seeker*. Dr. Wheelis practices psychoanalysis in San Francisco.

D0049710

ALLEN WHEELIS

THE MORALIST

Penguin Books Inc
Baltimore • Maryland

Penguin Books Inc
7110 Ambassador Road
Baltimore, Maryland 21207, U.S.A.

First published by Basic Books, Inc., New York, 1973
Published by Penguin Books Inc, 1974

Printed in the United States of America

The author wishes to express gratitude to Alfred A.
Knopf, Inc., and Hamish Hamilton Ltd. for permission
to reprint from *The Rebel* by Albert Camus, translated
by Anthony Bower. Copyright © 1956 by Alfred A.
Knopf, Inc. Copyright © 1953, Editions Gallimard.

CONTENTS

I

Nihilism

IF God is dead, says Ivan Karamazov, everything is permitted. He is in despair at the torture of children but, without God, finds no base in reason on which to condemn torturers. Nor do we. The anguished cry of the moralist announcing nihilism has become the dictum of our age: everything is permitted. If God is dead our standards are necessarily manmade, are therefore arbitrary in that no such standard can be endowed with the right to disallow opposing standards. No standard, therefore, holds authority beyond the force with which it is imposed. "How many divisions does he have?" said Stalin, upon being warned not to incur the disapproval of the Pope.

We do not say these things out loud, nor even think them clearly, yet they have seeped into the fabric of our age, permeate it utterly. Our official pieties have become platitudes; we no longer dare walk in the streets. And millions of us who never heard of Ivan Karamazov, who know not what nihilism means, know very well that everything is permitted, and proceed demoniacally to prove it.

Even our atrocities become more atrocious. The suppression of the Easter Rebellion of 1916 was brutal, but when we look back on the faded photographs of those executions—the uniformed riflemen aiming at the white marker pinned over the heart, the officer with saber raised, the prisoner blindfolded, erect against the wall, the priest standing by—we sense a moral form, an honor still unextinguished by the evil in which it is forever embroiled and made to serve, an honor which now seems quaint, long ago, unbearably lost. The pictures we bequeath to our grandchildren show soldiers bayoneting at random on the racecourse at Dacca, massacres in Biafra, death factories in Europe: Belsen, Auschwitz, Treblinka, Katyn Forest, Babi Yar, nameless unchronicled camps in Siberia—the list is endless. And endless, too, the heaps of naked bodies pushed out of life without ceremony—no rites, no portent, just bulldozed like garbage into the lime pits. Everything is permitted.

The mood of this work is that some things are not permitted, that there are immanent standards, of man's making but not of man's design, that they are, therefore, to be discovered but not created, that though not absolute they change but slowly, that to live by them is what is meant by being human. Such standards transcend our knowing, are guides to lead us, not we them, are rules which we must seek to find, not presume to enact. There is a path to follow, the course of which we cannot foresee, a plan of which we may have intimation but can never master. Whirl need not be king. Something draws us as by an invisible hand—not God, but the advancing edge of our being which goes before awareness. Arrogance of knowing is our sin and creates our greatest danger. To have believed in a God who rules the world was an illusion, but we gain nothing in losing it if we reincarnate God in ourselves; and we do so whenever we think we can know all.

Having lost God we must not claim his position, must accept that we live still, and always, in a world as much beyond our encompassing as when God ruled, and that if ever by miracle of progress the world in which we live now should all be known, the world in which we then would live would have so grown that beyond the limits of the then known would lie again as large a fraction still unknown and unknowable.

There is something vulgar in the heart of man. It is always with us. Spirit gains no final victory. Sometimes spirit doesn't even try, for the vulgar thing may appear as earthy humor, innocent, beguiling. Listen to the Boy Scouts in chow line: "Beans, beans, the musical fruit; the more you eat the more you toot." Listen to the rich Texan in the Four Seasons: "I said a *thick* steak." "This one is three inches, sir. How thick do you require?" "Hell, just cut off his horns and wipe his ass and bring him on in." It's funny and warm and, as we say, human. It moves on easily to something crass. Listen to the sailors out on the town: "What a dog!" "She don't have to be beautiful. Just cover her face with a flag and fuck for Old Glory." It becomes something mean, the treating of a person as a thing to be used for the purposes of another. Listen at the urinal in the Greyhound Bus Station in Baton Rouge: "She was like out of it. I got her stood up on her knees on the edge of the bed. Turned on the light for the view. First I fucked her in the cunt. Then I dropped her knees to the floor, she didn't even notice. I spread her legs and let her have it in the asshole. Rammed her. She cried a little but didn't yell, and I come out bloody and covered with shit. Then I sat her up on the bed and fucked her face. Looked like she'd been eatin' brown gravy."

There is something terrible in the heart of man. Spirit rises above it, but the terrible thing remains there below. We may ignore it, particularly if we are fortunate and privileged, may treat it as a bit of disorder in an otherwise elegant room. Oh we see it, we say, but should not dwell on it. To what purpose? The beauty of the room is more striking and more important. We lie: the house which contains this elegant room with its little disorder contains also a back room where blood flows, where screams sound in the night. Where is that room? we ask. We've never seen it. How fortunate. How very fortunate not to know the back room of our own house. But we must not boast of such ignorance; the newspapers diagram it every day. Listen to the news from Dacca: "As a frenzied, shouting mob of 5,000 Bengalis screamed encouragement, young Mukti Bahini guerrillas methodically tortured four suspected Pakistani quislings. For thirty minutes, the guerrillas battered the bound bodies of the helpless prisoners with kicks and karate blows to their heads and genitals. Quietly and systematically, they began stabbing their victims over and over again—all the time carefully avoiding the prisoners' hearts. After more than ten minutes of stabbing, the grisly performance seemed at an end. The soldiers wiped the blood from their bayonets and began to depart. But before they left the scene, a small boy—perhaps a relative of one of the victims—flung himself on the ground next to a prisoner's near-lifeless body. In an instant, the guerrillas were back, kicking the boy and beating him with their rifle butts. And as he writhed, the child was trampled to death by the surging crowd." [1] Listen to the news from Saigon:

Nihilism

Vietnamese prisoners are dropped to their deaths from helicopters in order to frighten other prisoners on board into telling what they may know about enemy activity. When a helicopter returns from such a mission one sees at the door shreds of flesh from prisoners who had fought to keep from being beaten out of the aircraft.[2] The crew consists of round-faced boys, a chubbiness of childhood still in cheeks so lately touched by loving mothers.

A cold wind plays with scraps of old newspapers, hurls cinders in an eye that wants now to look outward, to see what it can see. The past was given over to the analysis of anxiety, the mastery of despair, the terrible tyranny of desire, the coming to terms. Consciousness was intensified, but illumined private chambers, personal depths. The world was stage for the struggles of one soul. It was not wasted, this age of psychology, though too prolonged: a lamp must be cleaned before it will illumine. Will it avail now for darkness?

The Modern Age declared that man can know the world by the unaided effort of reason, that the conditions and institutions of social life can be shaped by reason to a course of progress. This vision has been lost. The optimism of the eighteenth century becomes the nihilism of the twentieth. Of the bright hope not a trace remains. Technology progresses, but for destruction as much as nurture. Our great gains in knowing and in power serve the same old mixture of good and evil. In goodness of heart we have gained nothing.

Moral certainty has disappeared, the Enlightenment mandate to reshape the world is remembered as in a dream. Utopias have become fatuous, revolutions breed tyranny;

7

tides of blood having risen in the cause of freedom recede, leaving empires of slavery. We abandon the world then and take up psychology. We turn from the effort to diminish evil, and go at the matter from the underside, alter the person, create adjustment, a capacity for insulated personal happiness in a world of injustice. Come away, said Yeats:

> Come away, O human child!
> To the waters and the wild
> With a faery, hand in hand,
> For the world's more full of weeping than you can
>   understand.

But this, too, comes to an end. We lose interest now in the journey of one man, gain interest in that immense journey in the course of which we are, each of us, but a flicker of awareness. How large a space can we illumine?

Life is the referent of value. What enlarges and enriches life is good; what diminishes and endangers life is evil. We put aside the question of *whose* life, for upon that reef the ships of Christ himself break asunder. Let us for the moment, our only moment of agreement perhaps, regard life inclusively, and agree that value refers to life. To poison the air is bad; to preserve an atmosphere we can breathe is good; and good and bad here refer only to the effect upon life. For if we conceive a lifeless planet we find no reason to prefer oxygen to methane; there is no better or worse, any old atmosphere will do, or none at all.

Those most concerned with good seek after certainty. More than others they know that designations of good may be arbitrary, may therefore be mistaken, and that mistaken good may prove to be evil, may generate monstrous consequences. And not only certainty do they seek, those persons in quest of the good, but some particularly ultimate and unchallengeable certainty; for they know that arbitrary and mistaken good may appear as self-evident truth, that many such truths have entered unexamined into our convictions, have in time been hallowed by tradition, have woven their patterns through our lives, have become sacraments, have dominated conduct from within, needing no enforcement, and so have held sway over human affairs for age after age of what we now call evil.[3]

Needing such certainty every age achieves it, and every certainty is eventually discredited. Throughout the Middle Ages God vouched for designations of good and evil. With the Modern Age, in a great burst of optimism, we came upon a new method of arriving at certainty, the scientific method, believed that the truths so achieved would endure forever. Newton's laws became the archetype of such sureness, and we hoped to apply the method which had yielded these presumably immutable laws to the behavior of men and of nations. Gradually this vision has faded, now is lost. The methods of physics do not encompass life, and the behavior of men cannot be reduced to causal formulations. Physical science itself, delving ever more deeply into the finest structure of matter, reaching in our times the tiniest jewels of the great clock, finds not predictability but indeterminacy; and the law of the inverse square, that very model of lawfulness, has had itself to be revised. We live now on the far and ragged edge of the Modern Age. The market for absolute truths, scientific or social, is in shambles. No one buys, not at any price; and moralists, knowing this but believing it nonetheless necessary that designations of good be certain, be derived from principles of unchallengeable and immutable truth, turn away in despair, sail white boats in blue bays, sniff out the clean air, become connoisseurs of wine, cultivate their gardens.

Meanwhile weapons of demonic and upward-leaping potency proliferate everywhere on the blue sphere. The holders of power act, and, without conviction in the principles which once shaped ends, their actions proceed toward whatever ends the means at hand are suited to, and the only value is the efficiency with which we do whatever it is that we do. We have gained systems analysis, lost the knowledge of good and evil.

Remembering our six thousand years of diary-keeping and all the evil therein recorded, all wrought in the name of goodness, we try to console ourselves, to think it better this way, better even that we drift into evil than march resolutely toward some good which as we reach it may transform itself into evil. But we are not consoled. We are lost.

We cannot again believe in certainty, will find no absolute, must indeed make sure we find no absolute, yet must somehow find heart to take up again a concern with what is good, with what is right and what is wrong. We must accept that the most careful designation of good will yet have in it something arbitrary, that the most basic principle we ever utter will yet be fallible, may prove in time false —including this very principle here stated, that we must try, that trying may make a difference.

The dog we love, on whom we lavish such care, is in the dining room alone, does not know I watch from another room. He looks at the food on the table, sniffs, hesitates, feels conflict. Will he take the food or turn away? I think he might do either, that neither is foregone. But I do not think he has awareness of choice. He endures conflict but does not illuminate it to the point of creating freedom.

The conduct of animals is given by nature, is neither good nor bad. Morality begins when consciousness expands and intensifies to the point of including the choice of act-ing in ways perceived to be significantly different. We gain awareness of our impulses, needs, of the field in which we move, of the persons affected, the things involved, and perceive options for action that will have different qualities and consequences. To kill or to befriend are equally ex-pressive of the nature of man. When one is designated right and the other wrong we have separated ourselves from nature, hold to a standard of our own making. What is that standard? What are the sources of morality? How are they subverted? Freedom, justice, brotherhood— these are our noblest words, and in their names we enact monstrous crime. Is it conceivable that some principle of behavior might yet be found that would not again and al-most instantly be put to the use of murder?

But there is *no* principle which could not be so sub-verted. Surely we know this, we who have killed so many in the name of love. Better we not even seek a principle immune to such subversion; there is none. Better we not seek a new morality: we could not improve on freedom and justice and love. Better, rather, we seek some gain in awareness, some shift or extension of empathy, which may enable us better to use what we already know about good and evil.

The more certain we are of the evil we attack, the more certain we become of the good. That for which we fight

11

becomes, because of our fighting for it, self-evidently right. And as we gain in certainty we gain in courage, in strength, in the willingness to sacrifice. It comes then to seem that we may not only resist evil but destroy it utterly. We are emboldened to demand unconditional surrender, and to achieve it we do things in the name of justice and freedom which later generations will see as crimes. So during World War II the democracies began to describe themselves with some truth as "free nations," but "some" truth became the whole truth, and soon we had so convinced ourselves of the absolute goodness of our "free" political institutions as to justify an absolute victory over fascist evil. The legitimacy of demanding such a victory justified, in turn, the destruction of Dresden and of Hiroshima.

Certainty is not to be had. But as we learn this we become not more moral but more resigned. We become nihilists. If we know nothing for sure, how ever can we know we are right? And if never can we know we are right, how can we act? We can live without truth if we must, but quietly. But to defend good and attack evil means killing people, and how can we do that without being sure? The longer we are paralyzed by this nostalgia for lost certainty the deeper our nihilism. To go back is not possible; to go on requires that we give up the demand for certainty, become willing to act in a field of probable goods and probable evils, "to fight a lie in the name of a half-truth." [4]

Once we leave the mythical realm of certainty and enter the real world where all is contingent and temporary, we find immediately, as a great bonus, that we are already beyond nihilism. We are not in chaos, as we had feared, but in some agreement. In the darkened theater the story unfolds: violent strangers enter the peaceful land, begin to steal the cattle, destroy the farms, and all around us we sense agreement as to what is good and what is evil. The consensus is theatrical, to be sure, but a little more; for as we leave the theater a man in the street is beating a child with a broken golf club, and we all know this is wrong. Agreement is never complete, never sure, but is more than a random throw, in any event is all we've got, so better we make something of it than give up in despair.

Nihilism is a fraud. Beneath the mournful trappings lies a base heart. Nihilism would have us believe it springs from affinity for truth, for goodness, for the progressive betterment if not perfectibility of man, would claim a special yearning toward these ends, an unusual readiness to act in their service, being prevented from so acting because it brings to the world, along with this idealism, a gaze so honest and penetrating that these goals are revealed as illusions. The world it sees is without meaning, without purpose, without point. To see it thus is annihilating, few can look: the easier course is denial, turning away, feeding on phantom hope, believing that something can be done, that good is different from evil, that effort may count.

Such is the genealogy of nihilism as offered by nihilism itself. It walks among us with mournful stride and inward gaze, a mein of tragic modesty, and just a trace of self-righteousness. It has been around for quite a while, we know it well. Is it not time now to make something of our observation that it leads so reliably to quietism? Do not we in the twentieth century know something about sham? Do we not know that findings may depend upon motives, and that a searching examination of motives must be illumined by the consequences that the findings in question tend to bring about? A relentless demand for truth, we are told, is the motive which leads to nihilism. We take note of this claim, but note also that nihilism finds that nothing can be done, that good and evil are ultimately indistinguishable, that all is vanity, and that vanity, along with everything else, is absurd. A covert fear of the risk of trying would be well served by such findings.

So is it *just* love of truth? Or does some failure of nerve add ardor to that love? How disengage such currents? As it happens, we have a proposal: let nihilists be required to earn a license. Each and every candidate for nihilism who acts to relieve suffering, to better the human lot, who takes all the risks of a life given over to such action—not just the risk of failure but the risk of making things worse, not just the risk of being shot but the risk of being a fool, of falling on one's face—will be given a license to teach us his vision of life as meaningless. All other candidates will be rejected as unqualified.

A sunny Sunday afternoon. Strollers jostle on the narrow sidewalk—children, dogs, teenagers, bicyclists, lovers, grandmothers. We enter a pastry shop. In a glass case sweets of all shapes and colors. Before us, a man, woman, and boy. The man is silent, withdrawn, intense. The boy exclaims at the marvelous sight, pulls forward on his mother's arm, puts hands on the glass. His mother pulls him back. The parents look long and hard, the child exclaiming, "Look at that one! Oh look at the red one, it's a sled! Look at the brown one! There's one like a squirrel!" Behind the counter are two young women with flaxen hair, all smiles and sexiness, dirndl dresses with low-cut blouses and blossomy bosoms. The mother points to a green confection: "How much is that?" is told eighty-five cents. She pauses, deliberates, points to another: "And that?" Again eighty-five cents. She glances at her husband who does not meet her gaze, turns back to the display, stares, finally looks again at her husband, who now gives an all but imperceptible nod. Soberly, ponderously, she orders three sweets, two cups of coffee, one glass of milk. The milk is served in a green glass, the coffee in white mugs with a blue band around the rim.

My wife and I order sandwiches and coffee, sit on the sunny deck over the water. The couple with the child sits at the next table. The man wipes the seat of the iron chair; I think he is preparing it for his wife, but she sits without bother on another. He sits precisely on the now clean seat, carefully pulls up trousers pressed to a knife-edge crease. His socks are nylon, stretched tight, his shoes of a dark mustard color, waxed to a mirror sheen, not a speck of dust. He wears a brown striped shirt, button-down collar, tightly knotted tie, suede vest, freshly pressed jacket. His wife, too, is in her Sunday best, but without such an edge of care. The little boy is in shined shoes, now dusty from the parking lot, white socks, short pants, navy blue jacket and tie. The man's face is thin, dark, suspicious; his hands, which are scrubbed clean, are rough and callused. I think he is a workman, and I think he is preoccupied with the money they have spent, wishes he had withheld assent to these extravagant sweets, had taken his family elsewhere. It was, I think, the loss of status he would have felt, backing out of this shop past people who really can afford it, which held him there. By pride was he trapped.

On the other side of us is a girl in a white blouse with long brown hair blowing in the wind, and a young man in

a yellow sport shirt, very big and husky. They are laugh-
ing, bending over the table, foreheads touching. A clown
appears on the deck with an accordion, a parrot on his
shoulder. The clown sings, does a little dance; the parrot
asks for money. Many people sit at tables. The atmosphere
is happy. From a house on the hill comes the sound of
music, the Wesendonck Lieder. The little boy stands on
the chair, lifts his hand to the hovering sea gulls which
swarm down for food. There is a warm breeze. I feel a
hand on my hand, look up to the eyes of my wife. The
bay is filled with sailboats—blue water, white sails,
red spinnakers, golden sunlight. The moment itself is
golden.

It ends suddenly. The boy's knee upsets the glass of
milk, it falls, breaks on the cast-iron chair. The snap of
glass and splash of milk is followed a moment later by another sound, something like the crack of a rifle. The boy's
head jerks back. After a moment he begins to cry. His father stares at him unspeaking, unmoving.

The two sharp sounds make a vacuum which sucks
away all other sound. All faces are toward the family, all
eyes on the man who now slaps the boy again, his hand
like a rapier, quicker than a reflex, the child can't see it
coming, there's no time to flinch: again that rifle shot, and
the boy's head jerks back. The outline of the father's hand
appears like a negative on his son's cheek, fingers white,
outlined in red.

There is a murmur of protest. Ladies whisper disapproval. The child cries, but seems to know that crying will
add to his punishment, stifles his sobs, chokes on them; his
shoulders shake convulsively. His mother is dismayed but
does not intervene, does not protest, wipes away his tears
with her napkin. I think the child feels her sympathy; she

is telling him that this is all that is safe, that she would do more if she could.

The man is carved in stone, impaling the boy on a murderous stare. Milk is splattered on the man's trousers. Drops of milk spread out on his shoes, form pseudopods which find no purchase on the waxed surface, can't sink in, withdraw, contract again into spherical droplets. Milk drips slowly through the filigree tabletop. The man moves not a muscle; his controlled fury does not subside. We would have thought he would begin to grumble, to wipe up the mess, to scold the child, but none of these things happens. His gaze remains fixed on the convulsed boy and his expression does not alter. A minute passes. The mother dabs at her son's face.

There it is again, that snake-striking swiftness, that rifle shot. The head jerks back, and again the negative of the hand on the now swollen face. The murmur grows louder: "What a shame!" "He didn't mean to do it!" "It was an accident!"

I turn away, cannot bear to look. The couple on the other side of us is silent. The girl has lowered her head, the young man is staring at the father, his shoulders hunched forward, muscles as if they would burst out of the yellow tennis shirt.

Where is nihilism now? Where that doctrine that all is permitted? It's not so. One more slap and this young man, I think, is going to throw this unhappy and dangerous father over the railing. Where now that maxim that all is absurd, that nothing matters? It's not true. We know a lot about good and evil, none of it for sure but some of it awfully well. There are perhaps thirty people on this deck, and every one of us is watching this family, and every one of us knows that what this father does is wrong.

It's not hard to understand him. We can fill in a twisted and victimized life, can take a point of view from which he must be seen with as much sympathy as we now see his child. But to understand is not to forgive—not unless we regard that which we understand as having been inalterably determined, in which case all is indeed absurd, for *our* reactions, whether of blame or forgiveness, would then be as determined as those of him whom we judge. However unfortunate his own childhood he yet is responsible, in the view of all who believe in freedom, for not inflicting such a childhood on his own son.

We know something also of goodness. This mother patiently wiping the boy's face, this is goodness. It wards off no blows, but gives some comfort; and her careful neutrality enables her to give this comfort without provoking greater violence. And this gentle chorus of protesting voices, the lamenting note urging moderation, representing that the boy did not mean to spill the milk, this is goodness. And the young man in the yellow shirt who looked so boyish before, and now so grown up, there is goodness in his passionate indignation. I watch the muscles move in his powerful shoulders and am less sure, however, of the goodness of what he is about to do.

I see it in mind's eye, watch it unfold. (Imagination is cheap, and moralists have it to spare. Action is all that moralists lack. Bear this in mind and make due discount as the action which here impends is exposed to criticism by the imagination of a moralist!) Another slap and this young man in one stride will stand beside the father, will start to speak; his throat will move, but no words will come. Inarticulate, he will reach out and take the father by the lapels of his perfectly pressed inexpensive jacket, will lift him out of his seat, up, up, as if he were a rag, till only the tips of his waxed and milk-spattered shoes touch the deck, then will find his voice, will say huskily, "Lay off the kid." But the father, dangling there in public humiliation from the massive hand, is not through. He is a rat of a man, has been cornered and kicked many times, knows tricks; and now that rapier-swift hand moves again, faster than the eye can follow, flicks inside the jacket and out again, makes four lightning jabs, and comes to rest finally only as the young man slumps, his chest unsheathing a four-inch blade. A few hours later the young man dies and a few months later the father goes to prison.

Has goodness been done? Has evil been combated? Or has the courage to stand up against evil made for greater evil? Maybe it won't happen; the young man has not moved. The imagined scene rationalizes quietism. Is there no middle ground? In the presence of such evil have we no option between not acting and acting too much?

Now comes the fourth slap, and the young man stands up. There is a commotion near the door. A chair falls. The parrot squawks, flutters through the air. The clown trips, falls on his face, gets up, chases after the parrot which utters obscenities. The clown hops on one foot then the other, chasing the sarcastic bird always just out of reach. Presently the parrot lands on the shoulder of the little boy who stops sobbing, turns to look at the parrot, then at his father. The clown weeps and wails, wrings his hands, "I can't catch him! He will fly out to sea! Help me, gentle people! Help me!" Then, regaining composure, he creeps toward the parrot in grotesque caricature of stealth. The two waitresses follow on tiptoe. The clown nears the boy, hesitates, afraid to make the final lunge.

Once more now the father's hand moves: this time the lightning dart catches the parrot entire, without flutter. The clown leaps forward: "Wonderful! Wonderful! Kind sir, how marvelous of you! How quick, how deft! Thank you, thank you, thank you!" takes the parrot, fixes the tether, does a little dance, begins to play the accordion. The waitresses with blossomy bosoms clean the milk from the table, make the man stand up, sponge off his jacket, wipe his shoes, call him a hero. They bring more milk, more coffee, bring for the boy a pastry "on the house," a cream puff in the shape of a teddy bear.

The arguments of nihilism fade. That desperate logic, that relentless forcing of one's self into an unbearable corner; we understand the words but no longer feel that strange push for absolute consistency, that intolerance of paradox, that mad demand that if X is good, X^2 must be better, and X^∞ best of all.

We cannot doubt the compassion of Ivan Karamazov for tortured children. "They must be atoned for," he says, "or there can be no harmony. But how? How are you going to atone for them? Is it possible? By their being avenged? But what do I care for avenging them? What do I care for a hell for oppressors? What good can hell do, since those children have already been tortured? And what becomes of harmony, if there is hell? I want to forgive. I want to embrace. I don't want more suffering. And if the sufferings of children go to swell the sum of sufferings which was necessary to pay for truth, then I protest that the truth is not worth such a price." [5] He finds no way of course to achieve, or even to conceive of, the harmony he seeks, and, lacking it, despairs, cannot bring himself to try

to save one child for the reason that he sees no way to save
them all.

Whence this mania of all or nothing? these anguished al-
ternatives? Why not, rather, all or none or some, and settle
for some? "We deny God," declares Nietzsche, "we deny
the responsibility of God, it is only thus that we will deliver the world." [6] Why so arrogant? God hasn't done
very well, but who are you, Herr Friedrich Nietzsche—
delirious insomniac wandering the heights above Rapallo
in winter rain, heartbroken over a Russian girl who chose
another—who are you to be so sure you will do better?
And when, pray tell, will you "deliver" the world? A
hundred years have passed. Forgive us if we no longer hold
our breath. Your message is too flamboyant for our taste,
takes itself too seriously. We feel closer to the girl who rejected you, who felt something vaguely dishonest in your
breast-beating raptures. [7]

These wild-eyed nihilists with their rapid breathing did
not discover the death of God, they publicized it. And
though they shouted the news we suspect that they did not
themselves accept it, but, all unknowing, were attempting
to create anew out of their own logic another absolute to
replace the one they had lost. We part company with
them. Not that we, with greater insight, have solved their
hysterical paradoxes; the paradoxes have become irrelevant. [8] We have gotten used to the death of God, have
stopped weeping, are no longer intent on resurrecting him
in the guise of a law of history or of politics or of morals.
Our faith has become modest. We cannot save all the children, but our dismay that God does not stand beside us,
lending us his strength, no longer blinds us to the awareness that with good will and effort we may save a
few. [9]

Every age must create anew its knowledge of good and evil. Conditions change and our deepest assumptions about life—those assumptions without controversy, so general, so much a part of the necessary field within which thought and feeling take place that, of them, like the air we breathe but do not see, we have no awareness—these too change. We attend to the curves on the graph of our times, for they define our problems; but slowly, like the unnoticed creep of glacial ice, those faint vertical and horizontal lines upon which the curves are drawn themselves twist into another dimension. The coordinates of our moral universe shift, honored maxims become historical oddities: I swear never to cut for a stone, says the young surgeon, but doesn't mean it, affirms only vague and tenuous continuity with the ethics of Hippocrates. Eternal verities become transient and grotesque errors: Thou shalt not suffer a witch to live.[10]

From the Medieval Age with its world view derived from Christian story we have passed into an age dominated by the belief that man can know the world by the unaided effort of reason; and that belief, yielding in science and technology ever-increasing knowledge and control, has, in morals, yielded a harvest so cruel and meager that we come to the verge of giving up, of turning over the moral order to technicians who will never ask is it right or wrong but only will it work. For the belief that reason can know the good, can design ways of achieving and securing it, has led in politics to ever more violent and destructive revolutions and counter-revolutions, to ever more vicious and oppressive tyrannies, while in morals it has led to nihilism.

"Man is but a foundling in the cosmos," writes Becker, "abandoned by the forces that created him. Unparented, unassisted and undirected by omniscient or benevolent authority, he must fend for himself, and with the aid of his own limited intelligence find his way about in an indifferent universe." [11] We must not forego the use of this intelligence, but must never again forget that it is limited. We know now that to pursue it without limit leads in public life to the police state with its bureaucracies of evil, and in our souls to the conclusion that everything is permitted, that nothing can be vindicated, and so to paradox and despair.

Where then, having lost God, can we find a reasonable ground for reasoning about good and evil?

II

Antitheses of Morality

OUR designations of good and evil are uncertain not only because we can never be sure what consequences will follow from our acts, but also because the effects and hence the meaning of these fallibly previsioned consequences will themselves change in time. We who designate the good are not fixed in our nature but evolving; the culture in which our goods and evils achieve their consequences itself moves with ever-increasing and now overwhelming swiftness; and the community which enjoys or suffers these consequences ever widens in extent and now is worldwide, though still forever breaking down at national borders. As no designation of good and evil can be absolute, neither can it be fixed; no law which is just now will be forever just, and no political institution designed to secure the good can remain the best means to that good.

Morality includes insight and action—insight into the nature and likely consequences of behavior in order to recognize good and evil, and action to secure the good and diminish evil. With either alone morality does not exist, for neither alone entails responsibility. A disembodied spirit unable in any way whatever to exert influence, though it might know good and evil, would not be a moral agent. Likewise the action of the tiger that kills and of the antelope that flees, neither having knowledge of good and evil, exists in a nonmoral realm.

That aspect of morality relating to insight we call good and evil; that relating to action, right and wrong. Our decisions of right and wrong determine good and evil for those who follow. Our most difficult moral problems are likely to be about right and wrong. We find much agreement in the recognition of good and evil but much dissension when men of good will, agreeing on what is evil, ask themselves, "What should we do?" Holland fought the German invasion, Denmark did not fight. Both were overcome and overrun, Holland with much loss of life, Denmark with virtually none. Which was right? Could it be that both were right? Or both wrong?

Morality begins with the antithesis of good and evil, and antitheses of one kind or another proliferate in moral deliberation forever thereafter: opportunism versus principle, force versus authority, jungle versus community, ethics of responsibility versus ethics of ultimate ends. We want to secure the good and avoid the evil, but every case is special; sometimes good appears as evil, and even more often evil as good. We need a principle whereby to recognize and to distinguish. Needing such a principle of good we always find it, and have then in its opposite a principle of evil, and thus a moral view. With it we seek after good and fight evil, until at some time later we look about and see that we have wrought such havoc and desolation in the name of goodness that we must call it evil. We discard then the old principle, find a new one and, in its opposite, a new recognition of evil, and set out once again, memories being short, with a new banner on another crusade.

Such conflict can never be ended, nor can morality ever be entirely clear and coherent. Without subordination to principle morality is not possible, yet there is no principle which in every situation is a reliable guide to moral behavior. "If we wish to live in the light of reason," writes Isaiah Berlin, "we must follow rules or principles; for that is what being rational is. When these rules or principles conflict in concrete cases, to be rational is to follow the course of conduct which least obstructs the general pattern of life in which we believe. The right policy cannot be arrived at in a mechanical or deductive fashion: there are no hard-and-fast rules to guide us; conditions are often unclear, and principles incapable of being fully analyzed or articulated. We seek to adjust the unadjustable, we do the best we can." [1]

Every discussion of morality must concern itself with two everlastingly opposed ways of viewing experience. *First:* Human life cannot be truly human unless it transcends itself. Love mediates this transcendence, gives us a referent of value which goes beyond our own lives, enables us to push on past the limits of self, of our own happiness, to find greater good in the welfare of others, to become willing to sacrifice our own good, at times even our lives, for others, even occasionally for others yet unborn. *Second:* Life constitutes its own purpose and own justification. Its worth is found, if at all, in the present. Value is immanent in experience, and there is no good so certainly or ultimately good as to justify the sacrifice of the present for the sake of a future which might secure that good.

The strongest advocacy of either view derives from its demonstration that the opposing view is illogical and incredible; for neither view, in pure form, can be made consistent by anyone genuinely concerned with goodness. The transcendent view leads to the utilization of men as means to future ends, to the tyranny of abstractions, eventually to terrorism. The true revolutionary, writes Sergei Nechaev in an extreme statement of the transcendent view, "despises and hates present-day morality in all its forms and motives. He regards everything as moral which helps the triumph of revolution. . . . All soft and enervating feelings of relationship, friendship, love, gratitude, even honor, must be stifled in him by a cold passion for the revolutionary cause. . . . Day and night he must have one thought, one aim— merciless destruction." [2] The immanent view leads to an ever-narrowing concern with self, to narcissism, to the mincing life before the mirror, to gourmet food and greasy lips, old clarets, young girls.

Advocates of the immanent view know, however, that the present can never be an instant, must always be of certain duration. How long then? With what span may one concern oneself and still act on behalf only of the present? Alexander Herzen, spokesman of the here and now, allows perhaps a lifetime, sanctions the struggle for liberty by and for people now enslaved. Each generation, he says, must live for itself. But a generation is twenty or thirty years, and within such span much sacrificing of present for future can take place. Likewise, the sternest advocate of principle, of the transcendent view, is likely somewhere to call a halt to carnage conducted in the name of future goodness. Not even Saint-Just could bring himself to guillotine them all.

Anyone willing to pursue either course wholeheartedly finds himself far from goodness, finds himself in the one case angel of God with flaming sword, in the other, beast in the jungle, in neither case a man, in neither case likely to anguish over sources of morality. Any genuine concern with morality, therefore, must give up hope of discrediting either view, must seek some way to live between them, to endure the tension, to accept the irreconcilability of contending claims while yet holding on to something of both, trying always out of disparate fragments to build a foundation both for living one's own unique and singular life as fully as possible and also for acting in behalf of others and of the future.

When in the course of evolutionary development our forebears, living only in the present, became men, they acquired self-consciousness, and thereby acquired also—without losing the life of the senses, of the flesh, of the here and now—a past and a future, and the awareness of choice. Having become men we can never go back, can neither disavow consciousness, become animal, and live only in the present, nor disavow flesh and live altogether in spirit, logic, and abstraction. The conflict is built into the condition of life; it is *with* this conflict, not *beyond* it, that we must struggle toward a moral life.

The transcendent view sees the suffering of mankind as remediable, sees starvation that could have been avoided, wars that need never have occurred, the destruction of one people by another that was not required by the nature of either. Radical solutions are possible, call upon us for vision, intelligence, will, and the readiness to sacrifice. The immanent view sees the basic problems of man as perennial and insoluble, inseparable from life itself. We may feel for others in their suffering, may care passionately and extend ourselves to help, do what we can. But what we can do will be little and transient; fundamentally nothing will change. Cure is not possible; temporary improvement is all that may be expected.

Those of the transcendent view are likely to be activists, to have conviction, to act with force, to be dangerous. "Any attempt," Berlin writes, "to explain human conduct in terms of, or to dedicate human beings to the service of, any abstraction, be it ever so noble—justice, progress, nationality— . . . always leads in the end to victimization and human sacrifice." [3] Those, on the other hand, who hold that life must be its own justification are always at the edge of apathy: nothing much can be done, cultivate your own garden, drink a little wine, seek out the beauty of life, turn up the music, try not to hear the cries of despair.

The transcendent view talks about principle, the immanent view about life. But when adherents of transcendence talk about the "life" of the immanent view, they are likely to use words like "opportunism." And when adherents of immanence talk about the "principles" of transcendence, they are likely to use such words as "abstractions."

The transcendent view is likely to be associated with the conviction that truth is available, that man can know the world and himself with certainty. In the Middle Ages the source of truth was God, speaking through Holy Writ and his deputies on earth; in the Modern Age, now ending, it is man's own reason, empowered by scientific method. The possession of absolute truth conforms equally to conservative and to radical positions. Royalist and Communist may differ on everything else, but agree on this one thing, that man may know the truth.

The immanent view is likely to associate itself with a disbelief in all absolutes, whatever their source, to hold that knowledge is more or less reliable, more or less objective, but never completely reliable, never wholly objective; that though some truths stand firmly as long-enduring monuments to man's ability to know, no such monument stands forever; that knowledge gained never owes all to the known, but always something to the knower; that both knower and known are in flux; that even if we should, magically, utter an absolute truth we would ourselves not know it, and no matter, for it would anyway in the next moment be false; that, therefore, even if we could now for some basic problem find a radical cure which could be guaranteed to work, it might, by the time it could be brought into existence, achieve in that already altered situation only more suffering and greater evil; that though we may make some things better we will never cure anything; that therefore we should do what we can and throw into prison all architects of paradise.

We are in our nature, tooth and brain, in the way we have come to be what we are, locked in the tension of this conflict which exists at every level, from the most primitive—eat it all now or save some for tomorrow—to the loftiest reaches of spirit. We must live with it, embrace the contending claims, never hope to be free, never come to rest, trying always to shape from the welter of experience a realm of goodness and of beauty, and trying equally to find ways of reducing pain and despair.

Absolute adherence to primary virtues may produce saintliness, but creates no force to oppose evil and no responsibility for achieving good. A force effective in oppos-

ing evil and in achieving good requires at times that consequences take precedence over virtue. Absolute adherence
to honesty does not concern itself with the consequences
of telling the truth; consequences are irrelevant for the reason that even if they could be foreseen as evil this knowledge could not touch the absolute good of honesty, could
not therefore make any difference. Truthfulness, according
to this ethic, stands alone: as nothing can invalidate it nothing need authenticate it.

All ethically oriented conduct is guided, writes Max
Weber, "by one of two fundamentally differing and irreconcilably opposed maxims: conduct can be oriented to an
'ethic of ultimate ends' or to an 'ethic of responsibility.'
This is not to say that an ethic of ultimate ends is identical
with irresponsibility, or that an ethic of responsibility is
identical with unprincipled opportunism. . . . [But] there
is an abysmal contrast between conduct that follows the
maxim of an ethic of ultimate ends—that is, in religious
terms, 'The Christian does rightly and leaves the results
with the Lord'—and conduct that follows the maxim of
an ethic of responsibility, in which case one has to give an
account of the foreseeable results of one's action. . . . In
numerous instances the attainment of 'good' ends is bound
to the fact that one must be willing to pay the price of
using morally dubious means or at least dangerous ones
—and facing the possibility or even the probability of evil
ramifications. From no ethics in the world can it be con-
cluded when and to what extent the ethically good purpose
'justifies' the ethically dangerous means and ramifications."

Every state is founded on force, every state asserts itself
as the sole legitimate source of the right to use violence;
the decisive means for politics, therefore, is violence. It
would be easy, Weber continues, if we could believe that

34

from good comes only good and from evil comes only evil, but "the world is governed by demons and . . . he who lets himself in for politics, that is, for power and force as means, contracts with diabolical powers and for his action it is *not* true that good can follow only from good and evil only from evil, but . . . often the opposite is true." It is the specific means of legitimate violence at the discretion of human associations, he writes, which determine the peculiarity of all ethical problems of politics. "He who seeks the salvation of the soul, of his own and of others, should not seek it along the avenue of politics, for the quite different tasks of politics can only be solved by violence. . . . Everything that is striven for through political action operating with violent means and following an ethic of responsibility endangers the 'salvation of the soul.' If, however, one chases after the ultimate good in a war of beliefs, following a pure ethic of absolute ends, then the goals may be damaged and discredited for generations, because responsibility for *consequences* is lacking. . . ."

Clearly Weber's own sympathies go out to the politician who, at the risk of achieving evil, struggles to achieve good and accepts responsibility for the consequences of his actions. The devil is old, he reminds us; grow old to understand him! What is decisive, he says, is a "trained relentlessness in viewing the realities of life, and the ability to face such realities and to measure up to them inwardly." The only possible harmony, he concludes, is that which is achieved by one man holding within one heart these irreconcilably opposed moral claims in such a way that he "is aware of a responsibility for the consequences of his conduct and really feels such responsibility with heart and soul. He then acts by following an ethic of responsibility and somewhere he reaches the point where he says: 'Here I stand; I can do no other.' That is something genuinely human and moving. And every one of us who is not spiritually dead must realize the possibility of finding himself at some time in that position. In so far as this is true, an ethic of ultimate ends and an ethic of responsibility are not absolute contrasts but rather supplements, which only in unison constitute a genuine man—a man who *can* have the 'calling for politics.' " [4]

Freedom is not one moral value among many, but the necessary condition for all morality.[5] Without the possibility of acting other than one did or does or might act there is no responsibility, and without responsibility no morality. Freedom derives from choice, and choice in turn from awareness—from a steadily growing consciousness of the world which, reaching eventually a certain extent and intensity, turns back upon itself to include the knower with the known, and in that awareness *creates* the possibility of acting this way or that. For the existence of options of which we have no awareness confers no freedom. It is only in having the choice, in *knowing* we can do this or that, that we begin to ask which is better, which is good, which is evil? The genealogy of morals, therefore, goes back to that evolutionary process of gradually extending awareness which reaches, in man, that reflexive intensity which creates the condition for freedom, which freedom in turn then creates the condition for morality.[6]

III

Goodness and Morality

W E are driven to seek meaning, and find it by discovering a necessary relation between our lives and some larger purpose. We explain by narrating.[1] When we have so explained something we have demonstrated that, from a given origin, it cannot be other than the way it is. A chance fragment of life, irregular in configuration, absurd in conclusion, is thus perceived to fit into a unique place in the cosmic puzzle. "In the beginning God created the heaven and the earth": so begins the Hebraic story. "In the beginning was the Word, and the Word was with God, and the Word was God": so begins the Christian story which, from Constantine until the Enlightenment, provided for the Western World the meaning and authentication of human life. These stories have lost all authority, remain with us only as legends. "The great efflorescence of history in the eighteenth and nineteenth centuries," writes Lionel Trilling, ". . . may be thought to have had as one of its unavowed aims to supply their loss. When God died, as by common consent he did, however slowly the explicit news of the demise reached us, history undertook to provide the beginnings which men once thought necessary to the authenticity of the world and themselves. Nietzsche says that the realization of the death of God had the effect of making all things, and man himself, seem 'weightless': the great narrative historians in some considerable degree maintained the weightiness of things by thickening the past, making it exigent, imperative, a sanction of authority, an assurance of destiny. The tale they told interpreted the sound and fury of events, made them signify *something*, a direction taken, an end in view." [2]

Such narrative history has all but disappeared. We no longer believe it. "To write the History of England as a kind of Bible"—this was Carlyle's goal in a time of crisis and uncertainty; "for England too (equally with any Judah whatsoever) has a History that is Divine; an Eternal Providence presiding over every step of it . . . ; guiding England forward to *its* goal and work, which too has been considerable in the world!" [3] Churchill in mid-twentieth century wrote such a history, but we see it as a monument to a faith which is now itself historical. Millions of those multi-volumed boxed sets distributed by book clubs rest inertly on our shelves. The titles thunder down at us, but stir no fervor, lift no hearts. History authenticates nothing, is itself desperately in need of authentication. For what we find in the past of all peoples—English, German, Russian, whatever—is such a record of folly and confusion, of nobility and absurdity and cruelty, as, on a smaller scale, characterizes our individual lives. It is just the sort of thing from which we seek escape into meaning if we can but find it. [4]

We enter then the age of psychology, seek authenticity for our lives through the unmasking of pretenses, the searching out of covert motivations. But the "completely analyzed person," that eminent fiction of our times, is no more able to authenticate his individual existence with the assimilated and presumably integrated fragments of unconscious bits and pieces of his individual past than is the most miserable neurotic among us. Psychology cannot lead us out of this desert. Indeed, the well-analyzed, well-integrated, well-dressed man in the gray flannel suit, with his liberal or even radical views, his experimental life style, is in the same miserable fix as are we all, smoother perhaps but just as confused and heartsick.

The data of psychotherapy are the qualities of psychological life as known by introspection to each of us—conflict, memory, desire, anger, sadness, guilt. To make a science of all this is to treat the ordinary weather of our days as reducible to determinable and determining cause, and this excludes freedom and responsibility. We can have it either way perhaps, but we cannot have it both: if in this scientific age we consider a science of the soul indispensable, we must pay for it in freedom; if we put freedom above everything else we must give up the science of sadness, and with it the right to regard our misery as an illness and the hope of getting it cured like an aching tooth.

Just now we are going through a backlash, are hoping to find in madness the authenticity we could not locate in even the best-analyzed sanity. But no one, as Trilling observes, who knows and takes seriously the day-to-day despair of the schizophrenic is likely to feel much hope in this direction. We turn back also, some of us, to religion, to Eastern religions this time which, being unknown, have not yet betrayed us. We turn to desperate fads, to drugs, mysticism, scientology, even astrology, that faded costume from the trunk of our medieval past. We turn back also to history, but now we take a longer view. We search for meaning in the past, not of a nation or of a race, nor even of mankind, but of life itself.

We have come an immense journey in darkness. We remember nothing. We did not act, but react. We snarled, fought, gorged, copulated, pushed on through age after age the sluggish chain of being. Lost, forgotten, we remember nothing. Nature led us, held our hand.

Gradually in those millions of years reaction becomes sensation, sensation becomes perception, perception becomes awareness. Our animal forebears did not live in a moral order: the conduct of life was given by nature, was neither good nor bad. Millennia slip by, falling after each other like leaves, and presently awareness becomes self-awareness, illumines options, creates choice. That man has a female I want; I could kill him and take her. What should I do? Which is better? Which is right? Which is wrong? Nature leaves us. No one holds our hand. To kill him or to spare him are equally expressive of what we are. So soon as one is right and the other wrong, some referent of action other than nature has been found.

As hunter and food-gatherer we lived still in a state of nature. If game was plentiful we flourished, increased in number; the increase in number increased the demand for game, whereupon game became scarce; and the dearth of food in time reduced the number of men. So man, like all other forms of life, lived in equilibrium with a natural environment of which he was a part, wandered the earth in small bands with stone axe and stone knife, eventually with the magic of fire, but still, for hundreds of thousands of years, in a state of nature.

With the beginning of agriculture and of the domestication of animals we lived no more in the world we found, but created the world we lived in. In the green valleys of the Tigris and the Nile we began to remember the past. Savages raided our villages. Once we had been as they, did not till the soil, might become again the wandering hunter. Remembering, we begin to compare: this is better than that. Awareness reaches the level of choice; freedom begins. Economically we left nature when we began to create our own environment; morally, when we began to perceive ourselves in others and to create out of that awareness the beginning of freedom.

Morality may be seen as a negation. In this view it does not prescribe what we *shall* do but what we may *not* do. Such moral rules are empty of purpose, do not specify goals to follow, ideals to guide us, but define categories of behavior which are not permitted. So conceived, morality is not in conflict with self-interest, for we may say of a man both that his conduct is motivated by his own needs and desires and also that he is moral. That is to say, he undertakes that his pursuit of self-interest not violate the rights of others. In this view the moral man is not to be defined as one who does good, though he *may* do a great deal, but as one who does not wrong others.

For most of us, however, negative morality is not moral enough. It's not enough, we would say, that a person do no wrong. There is so much evil and pain, a good man must do something about it; and a moral law which would designate as good a man who does nothing is inadequate. We want more. And so we have *Love thy neighbor as thyself*, and the ideal of sacrifice: *Greater love hath no man than this, that a man lay down his life for his friends*. The moral man, according to this view, is he who does good for others. The rules of such morality are not abstract: they define the good, prescribe value, formulate purpose, create an ideal. So conceived, morality conflicts with self-interest, calls upon us to forsake self-interest for the interest of all.

Positive morality cannot abide strangers, cannot accept "we and they," wants all to be "we," insists that strangers are really neighbors whom we must love; and if, as may happen at times, they should be so degenerate and vicious that we cannot love them, then we must reform them, shape them, bring them back to true values, so that we then can love them. This is the missionary spirit, the ethic of action, of going out of one's way, often at great sacrifice, to do good as "we" define the good. Of course those who most need our help are often unaware of their need, may in their benightedness resist us; we may have to use force. Sometimes, indeed, we have to kill a great many in order to save the rest. So we saved the Aztecs whose sacerdotal cannibalism, according to Prescott, "suggests ideas so loathsome, so degrading to man, to his spiritual and immortal nature, that it is impossible the people who practice it should make any great progress in moral or intellectual culture." [5]

Such, also, is the morality of Romanticism, of Jean-Jacques Rousseau who resolved "to burst asunder the bonds of opinion, to do boldly everything which seemed good to him, and to pay no heed to the judgment of other men," and who declared the morality implicit in this arrogance to be "perhaps the greatest revolution, or at any rate the one most useful to virtue, ever conceived by man." [6]

Negative morality accepts the existence of strangers, knows there always will be a "they," that "we" and "they" will be divided at times on the most basic issues, unable to agree on the nature of the good. Because of the inevitability of such division and opposition, negative morality urges the mutual acceptance of abstract rules of fair conduct in order that individuals and groups of divergent values, conflicting purposes, may live together without destroying each other.

That view which sees morality only as positive ends always in contradiction, often in despair. "For if any principle has an inalienable right to be observed," writes Bishop Kenneth Kirk, "*every* other principle would have to be waived if the two came into conflict in a given case. . . . It seems that we have reached a point at which the whole ambitious structure of moral theology is revealed as a complete futility." [7]

Negative morality does not oppose the extension of love to an ever wider neighborhood, does not stand against generosity or self-sacrifice or the active doing of good; it opposes only the doing of those things, good or bad, whatever the motive, which infringe the rights of others. It issues a prohibition to one's self in order to protect others, says no to certain things one might wish to do. But though it authorizes no positive act, it does not oppose the doing of good provided we stop doing it when the one to whom it is being done becomes unwilling to accept it. The doing of good to others against their will, it asserts, has always been, and remains, our greatest evil.

A certain unease remains, a nagging feeling that morality can't simply be negative, that it must somehow entail a positive act. Positive morality tends to creep back, first as if but to enrich negative morality, to give it heart, but eventually to take over. *Thou shalt not kill* imposes on each of us the responsibility of curbing aggression short of murder. But some people won't, and what about them? Does not the prohibition which we heed contain the im-

plicit sanction to control those others who do not heed? Is
not the commandment, therefore, in effect, *Thou shalt not
kill and shall permit none other to kill?* And does not such
sanction to control others constitute positive morality?
The most peaceful community has a cop, and what is he
doing if not achieving good by attacking evil?

At this point the concept of different levels of organization, of hierarchic order, is crucial. The abstract rules
apply to individuals, are simple prohibitions, have no positive content, implied or otherwise; the enforcement of
these rules is the responsibility of the social order. It is the
responsibility of each individual not to kill, not to steal, not
to bear false witness; but it is not his responsibility to prevent you from doing so. *You* are responsible for preventing *yourself* from doing these things; and if you fail, the
responsibility for enforcement devolves, not upon an individual, but upon the social order. The policeman, that is,
must not act as an individual but only as agent of society;
conversely, the individual must not act as policeman.

All of the foregoing considerations, addressed to the morality of individual behavior, apply also, at a higher level in
the hierarchy, to the behavior of nations. A positive morality calls upon nations to do good; a negative morality calls
upon them to observe limits. Nations inspired to do good
call up their armies, bring pressure upon their allies, alert
their fleets, and set out to enact in the world good as they
know the good. Russia spreads communism, the United
States spreads democracy; and if we continue in this missionary spirit, and try hard enough, we may destroy the
world in our will to save it, as the zealot may kill his
neighbor in a fervor to redeem him.

To those who conceive of the morality of nations in
such positive terms, a nation may be guided by self-interest

or by morality, but not both. "History and our own achievements," said President Johnson in 1965, "have thrust upon us the principal responsibility for protection of freedom on earth. . . . No other people in no other time has had so great an opportunity to work and risk for the freedom of all mankind." [8] And *The New York Times* quotes an American pilot over Vietnam: "I do not like to hit a village. You know you are hitting women and children. But you've got to decide that your cause is noble and that the work has to be done." [9]

Reinhold Niebuhr assumes that morality is positive, that there isn't any other kind, that individuals must obey the law of love and sacrifice: "From the viewpoint of the author of an action, unselfishness must remain the criterion of the highest morality." [10] He assumes, likewise, that the morality of nations, if it exists at all, must be of the same kind, and argues that such morality is inappropriate to nations for the reason that nations are but trustees for individuals and have not the right to be unselfish with the interests of others. Nations cannot, therefore, be moral. Arthur Schlesinger argues the same line: "The individual's duty of self-sacrifice and the nation's duty of self-preservation are in conflict; and this makes it impossible to measure the actions of nations by a purely individualistic morality. . . . Those who see foreign affairs as made up of questions of right and wrong begin by supposing that they know better than other people what is right for them. The more passionately they believe they are right, the more likely they are to reject expediency and accommodation and to seek the final victory of their principles." [11] These arguments assume that the only morality is of the "doing good" or "self-sacrificing" kind, and assume also that the state is not an entity with its own unique attributes and functions, hierarchically separate from the individual, with its own capacity for moral and for immoral action, but only an agent of the individuals who comprise it.

But nations are entities, not congeries, and there exists for nations a negative morality, exactly comparable to the negative morality of individuals, which would define those categories of national behavior which, however desirable or even justifiable in certain circumstances they may seem to be, are not permitted, and from which each nation is responsible for restraining itself. So conceived, there would be no inconsistency in saying both that a nation's policy is guided by national interest and that the action of the nation is moral; for such a statement would mean only that the nation is motivated by considerations of its own welfare and security, but that whenever such considerations direct it to an action forbidden by voluntarily accepted abstract rules of fair conduct among nations, it foregoes that action. National interest thus determines national behavior except when national interest conflicts with moral prohibition; when such conflict occurs, prohibition takes precedence over interest. And, again comparably to the situation at the individual level, if one nation does *not* so control itself, it is not the responsibility of another nation to act as policeman, but of an organized association of nations which constitutes a supranational entity hierarchically removed from the nations which comprise it, as one nation is removed from the individuals who compose it.

"There is only one thing," writes Joseph Fletcher, "that is always good and right, intrinsically good regardless of the context, and that one thing is love. . . . Love and justice are the same, for justice is love distributed, nothing else." [12]

Would that it were true, but the long record of crime in the name of love, all those holy crusades, indicates that love is a poor criterion of justice. Nor has any other good a better claim—not equality, not brotherhood, not even liberty.[13] We must realize, writes F. A. Hayek, that rules of justice are in the nature of prohibitions. "Injustice is really the primary concept and the aim of rules of just conduct is to prevent unjust action. . . . Free men who are allowed to use their own means and their own knowledge for their own purposes must therefore not be subject to rules which tell them what they must positively do, but only to rules which tell them what they must not do. . . . The rules of just conduct thus merely delimit the range of permissible action but do not determine the particular actions a man must take at a particular moment." [14]

The field of ethical thought is so divided: on the one side love of others, on the other respect for the rights of others. Positive morality is revolutionary, negative morality is judicial; the one is embodied in Rousseau, the other in Hume. Positive morality dictates our purposes; negative morality leaves purposes for us to determine, but sets limits which guard the freedom of others to pursue *their* purposes, limits which our purposes, whether selfish or unselfish, are not permitted to exceed. The one asserts love and tends to be religious, the other asserts justice and tends to be secular. The one appeals to compassion, the other to fair play. Positive morality is proud, believes great things may be achieved, raises banners, sets out on crusades; negative morality is modest, believes some things may be achieved but never a radical cure, is unmoved by banners, declines crusades. One is a striving to achieve, one a taking pains to avoid. We have a spontaneous preference for the positive, and the greater our generosity and warmheartedness the stronger this preference; the negative settles on us as a dismal fog. The one appeals to our creativity, our trust in the heart, our willingness to risk, our hope to transcend ourselves and merge with others; the other appeals to our cautiousness, our trust in law, our separateness.

The illusion in this dilemma is that these two good things, love and justice, contend for the same prize, the supreme right to guide our lives; and the key to the conflict is the recognition that they serve different goals, are complementary, depend upon each other, are equally necessary. We are confused by using one word, morality, for both; for clearly we cannot have *two* moralities. Pious Sundays followed by rapacious weekdays, soldiers who are good boys at home but murderers of unarmed civilians in foreign jungles—this is just what morality is meant to prevent. The two good things need different names: *positive morality is simply goodness, negative morality is simply morality*.

Goodness and morality are equally necessary to human life. Goodness without morality is dangerous in the extreme; morality without goodness is sterile. Both derive from our ability to see ourselves in others; but from this primary identification they develop along different lines: one leads to love and thence to goodness, one to respect and thence to morality. Goodness is spontaneous, generous, outgoing, is marked by compassion, empathy, unselfishness, at times by self-sacrifice, is symbolized by Christ who said: "This is my commandment, that ye love one another, as I have loved you. Greater love hath no man than this, that a man lay down his life for his friends." Morality is reflective, judicial, marked by the recognition of limits which define our freedom. This freedom is limited and precious, has been hard won, and we will not give it up, would die to uphold it. A free man is not a slave who has escaped his master; such a man is but a runaway slave who may be caught and returned to servitude. A free man, though he may be overpowered, may be killed, cannot be reduced to servitude; something in him asserts freedom as an inviolable right. It is not negotiable. He does not *ask* that others respect this right, he *requires* it; and it is ultimately his willingness to die for this freedom which forms the basis of his demand that others respect it.

Mankind enters history as free men and as slaves. As far back as we can see, this division has never been absent, remains with us today. There was a time we cannot remember when manlike creatures wandered the earth in a state of nature. They did not live alone but in groups, and unlike other animals who fought each other and parted, they fought each other and killed. Those who were weak, or were unwilling to kill, perished; those who were both strong and willing to kill survived, and spared some of the weak who would accept servitude, and so began the condition of master and the condition of slave.

It is not to those ancient masters that we owe the beginnings of morality, but to those ancient slaves. Masters then as now are content with the way things are; it is slaves who make for change. Nietzsche was right, Christianity is a slave morality; but there is no other kind. All morality goes back to that rebellion with which the condition of servitude is refused. The runaway slave simply escapes, but rebellion asserts a value with which morality begins.[15]

It is in rebellion we see most clearly that primary ability to recognize ourselves in others which is the common source of both goodness and morality. The slave who runs away runs for himself alone, but the slave who stands up against his master rebels for all. The rebel has recognized a brotherhood with those beside him who bear the same chains, suffer the same lash. He knows he will die but finds courage to rebel because he acts in the name of all. He attacks the privilege of a few by authority of a right he ascribes to all. So the beginnings of goodness lead to that solidarity with others which makes possible the rebellion which creates the beginnings of morality, which in turn supports goodness, which provides then the basis for further rebellion. Behind us millions have hung from crosses, died in dungeons; our bones must ache for those whose bones were broken on the wheel.

A good man may be immoral. We must grant that those missionaries who sanctioned the murder of savages, those bishops who decreed the burning of witches, were good men, wanting to save those about to be damned, to bestow true faith, to give great gifts. Many of them, like Christ, gave up their own lives to such unselfish ends. They were nevertheless immoral in that they did not respect the rights of those who believed otherwise. An immoral man, likewise, may be good. The essence of the rights protected by morality is that they *are* rights, not privilege, that they may not therefore be either bestowed or withheld. Robin Hood is immoral in not acknowledging for the rich those rights which belong to all, yet good in the generosity and selflessness with which he distributes spoils to the poor. There is no motive, not even the most selfish, with which morality necessarily conflicts; and there is no motive, not even the most holy, with which conflict is not possible.

Morality is not a motivation but a limit; not endeavor or process or purpose, but a wall. It is not meant to *make* anything happen, but to *prevent* certain kinds of things from ever happening. To inquire of a person, "Is his life determined by selfishness or by morality?" makes no sense; for it ascribes alternativity to traits which, though either may be present without the other, may yet both be present or both absent. When we know of a person that he is selfish we still do not know whether he is moral. He is moral if, in those circumstances in which his selfish impulses conflict with the rights of others, those rights, installed in his own conscience as prohibitions, constitute a barrier which confines the behavior to which selfishness impels him within limits which protect others. Of such a person we may say, "He is moral" without diminishing the force with which we may say, also, ". . . and utterly selfish." We need not admire him, would not have him as a friend, yet must respect his morality; it protects us from his unfortunate nature.

Likewise, when we know of a person that he is of loving and generous disposition, one who though himself hungry gives us his last bit of food, who would lose his life to save ours, we still do not know whether he is moral. He is moral if his loving impulses are reliably confined within limits which protect the rights of others, immoral if he believes that the goodness of his goals, the sincerity and the selflessness with which he pursues them, gives him license to violate those limits. A pure heart guarantees nothing, may sorrowfully send legions of heretics to the stake. To know the good is a dangerous thing; to know it for sure is usually fatal for somebody.

Morality is designed to secure the greatest possible freedom for everyone compatible with the restraints necessary for group life. It is not enthusiastic about human nature: although it knows the nobility and generosity of which we are capable, it knows even better our capacity for evil, addresses itself to that evil, builds a structure to contain it. It is concerned but indirectly with good, holds that if evil is controlled, goodness will have its best chance to flourish. A moral man is he who observes those rules of just conduct which have been defined by the traditions and the laws of the society to which he belongs. When we are so fortunate as to see a man risk his life to save a stranger, we do him and his gallantry a disservice to call it moral. It is an act of nobility and goodness, whereas morality is a structure of restraint.

These considerations apply in exact parallel to the behavior of nations. A nation may follow a policy of self-interest and yet, by virtue of respecting the rights of other nations, be moral; and a nation may sacrifice self-interest to help other nations and yet, if it does not respect those rights, be immoral.

IV

Slavery and Rebellion

LET us imagine a perfect moral order, a village out of the dreams of childhood: half-timbered houses with thatched roofs, a steepled church and a white school, a green valley surrounded by snow-capped mountains. We are enchanted by belled cows with enormous liquid eyes grazing on steep hillsides, we admire the neat farms, the clean streets. We are happy to visit, it's like coming home. We like the friendly dignified people, watch them in their daily lives, their work, the way they talk and walk and go about the cleaning, the marketing, the looking after children, the kneeling in church, the making of music. There is no violence: disputes are arbitrated or litigated, the loser grumbles but accepts. People sleep well at night. A policeman walks the streets twirling his stick, but has nothing to do. The behavior of each person conveys respect for the rights of others as these rights are defined by tradition and law.

The town we have imagined, consonant with our own values, is in nineteenth-century Switzerland, but for exemplariness of moral order might just as well have been in Egypt in the ninth century B.C. For a moral order of that time and place may be conceived to have functioned just as

57

well, though its rules of just conduct would specify different limits depending upon whether one were a woman, a slave, a prisoner, or a stranger, might entail the ritual sacrifice of children. Morality is the structure with which society controls evil; but the nature of evil changes with time, so no moral order can be absolute or fixed. A moral order conserves, does not seek progress, tries to project itself unaltered into the future. It does nevertheless change, though slowly, so always is relative.

Generosity and love and self-sacrifice may accomplish vast good within any moral order without changing the order itself. Rebellion, as an attempt to change the rules of which morality consists, is therefore immoral, violates the moral order in the hope of changing it. It is the desperate exception, involves murder in the name of a good higher than the existing order can conceive. The rebellion of a slave strikes not simply a master but the moral order which sanctions slavery, so may in time change that order into one which prohibits slavery. Thus moral progress comes from immoral acts.

Before, however, we rush to endorse murder in the name of higher good, which is the very spirit of the twentieth century, we must note that rebellion usually becomes revolution, installs other masters for the ones destroyed, and that the change is not progress. The slave begins by demanding justice, writes Camus, and ends by wanting to wear a crown.[1]

The world is made up still of masters and slaves. The tendency of civilization, whether or not it ever diminish evil, places evil at an ever greater distance from those of us with means. The master stands over his one slave; with twenty slaves a deputy gives the orders, and the master forgets he owns a whip. In our time we can forget even that we own slaves, for we have found ways to confer upon them freedom, with all its legal trappings, yet keep them as slaves. Our achievement is in the nature of magic, pulling altruistic bunnies out of the black hat of self-interest. We have relieved ourselves of the guilt and responsibility of slave-owners, while retaining our privilege of exploitation; for rather few of us white-skinned people in the northern part of the western hemisphere claim and receive most of the world's goods, and rather more of us with darker skin work in the fields and factories of the rest of the world and receive but a fraction of the world's goods.

We deplore this inequity but disclaim responsibility, refer to "backward" or "underdeveloped" countries, as if they were pursuing their own independent destinies in their own retarded ways. Often we cast ourselves in the role of good neighbor, help them with loans, with technical experts. Yet "we" and "they" are not independent entities but one economy: we eat what they grow, wear what they sew, take from them all they produce and give them a bit of what we produce, and by this constant exchange and growing interdependence constitute one enterprise. Europe in the Medieval Age, encastled, unaware the outer reaches of the world, could disclaim responsibility; but in the sixteenth century Cortés and Cook and Magellan introduced us, and since then our interrelatedness has constantly increased. The world now is one economy. On an eighteenth-century plantation in Virginia, with its manor house and stables, its slaves and slave quarters, the master did not hold the whip; he listened to music, studied French, traveled, pondered Hume's *Enquiry Concerning the Principles. of Morals*. So do we still. The plantation has grown larger, the United States is the most opulent manor house in the world, our slaves work mostly in distant fields, we keep only a few around the house. We no longer visit the slave quarters; it's not necessary, we have excellent managers, experts in efficiency, sanitation, morale. They take care of things. We hear at times of rebellions, of famines, of savage fighting between slave factions, but we must not expect the world to be perfect. Doubtless our scientists are improving conditions all the time.

One of our noblest documents of freedom is Mill's essay "On Liberty," yet in defining the scope of freedom Mill finds it appropriate to "leave out of consideration those backward states of society in which the race itself may be considered in its nonage. The early difficulties in the way of spontaneous progress are so great, that there is seldom any choice of means for overcoming them; and a ruler full of the spirit of improvement is warranted in the use of any expedients that will attain an end, perhaps otherwise un-attainable. Despotism is a legitimate mode of government in dealing with barbarians, provided the end be their im-provement, and the means justified by actually effecting that end. Liberty, as a principle, has no application to any state of things anterior to the time when mankind have be-come capable of being improved by free and equal discus-sion. Until then, there is nothing for them but implicit obe-dience to an Akbar or a Charlemagne, if they are so fortunate as to find one." [2] All this may sound eminently reasonable to Europeans—to all those, Mill says loftily, "with whom we need here concern ourselves"—but it does not seem reasonable to "barbarians." What is most barbarous about us, they say, is that in fact we are slaves; and that tiny island of white slave-owners whereon Mill sat in his elegant well-appointed study and wrote so movingly of freedom became the richest country in the world by exploitation of our labor.

Morality comes easy for masters, its negative quality suits them fine, its prohibitions do not pinch. They respect tradition, do not seek change, think in terms of limits, are concerned to protect existing freedom by scrupulous regard for the rights of others. They assert that goodness is to be achieved, if at all, not by fighting for it—for they point out how variously the good is conceived and that he who would positively achieve it will eventually impose it by force—but by each person's holding himself responsible for *not* doing evil.

Slaves are unimpressed. They observe that good and evil are defined by the existing moral order within which they are victims. Their lives are dominated by something they *know* to be evil which yet is sanctioned by authority. Evil, therefore, is legal, and the wrong to slaves cannot be redressed by calling upon authority to enforce rules of just conduct; for it is these rules themselves, arising out of the traditional values obtaining in that society, which permit masters to do exactly what they are doing. If the slave is to right his wrong he must rebel—that is, become immoral in the name of a value higher than morality. His behavior conforms then to an ideal moral order which does not yet exist but to which his immoral act may give birth.

Ivan Karamazov describes the owner of an estate of two thousand souls, a sportsman who, his favorite hound having been injured by a serf boy of eight, has the child stripped and, in front of the child's mother and all the assembled servants, sets the hounds upon the boy who is torn to pieces.[3] The morality of masters would see this as a violation of the rules of just conduct and would call upon the state, as the only legitimate coercive power, to achieve observance of these rules. And this, in fact, is what was done: "I believe," Ivan remarks ironically, "the general was afterwards declared incapable of administering his estates."

Slaves are not satisfied by such justice. If they concern themselves with morality at all they feel that the moral order which permits such incidents is itself evil. Why did we stand by? they would say. There are hundreds of us, but one of him. We could have killed him on the spot—or could simply have refused. Why did we do nothing? Because the social order which designates us slaves, and the morality which supports that order, has entered into our very souls, has achieved its end that we accept ourselves as slaves. That's why we stood by helpless while the boy was killed. The moral order which requires us so to regard ourselves is itself evil and must be overthrown.

The immoral slave, declaring himself right in the judgment of an ideal moral order, takes up arms, begins to commit murder.[4]

A morality of abstract principle, if positive, leads to rational and systematic murder, to contradiction and nihilism, eventually to the police state. Moral principles which are abstract, therefore, must be negative, must describe a wall which limits each of us, thereby protecting all. The aims of rebellion are profoundly positive and must, therefore, be tangible and immediate. The slave standing up against his master seeks redress for present humiliation, affirms dignity, and so creates value. Masters do not, however, defer to slaves; and slaves, having stood up, become men, and the contest is fatal. The slave is usually killed, and existing morality is saved. Occasionally the slave strikes down the master, and the moral order changes. If, then, intoxicated by success, the slave elevates his achievement into abstract principle, and proceeds with murder as means to the end of eliminating injustice throughout the world, his rebellion betrays the value it engendered, leads to contradiction, nihilism, and terror.[5]

V

Force and Authority

RIGHT derives from custom, and our particular customs, we like to assume, have been ordained by God. Then we travel; and custom, everywhere different, loses claim to God's authorization. What custom is, it just happens to be, and the right which it defines is arbitrary, has no more authority than we give it. Why then, we begin to wonder, should we give it any at all? *The* right becomes conventional right, which invokes the idea of a right above convention, which could be none other than "natural" right. And what is that? Why, the interest of the stronger. With sudden insight, then, we may perceive conventional morality to be the strategy of the weak against the strong: so long as it retain the sanction of general acceptance it protects sheep from wolves; for wolves will be guided by the prevailing rules, which in turn derive from the customs of sheep. Woe to sheep when wolves study morals!

The Sophists were not Athenians, they *came* to Athens. In their travels they learned how customs differ, and they taught us that no customary order has divine authorization. "Concerning the gods," wrote Protagoras, "we know not whether they exist or no. The matter is very obscure and moreover the life of man is short." How, then, can we ever find ground for repudiating the great and successful crime? If Alexander and his armies and their way of life conquer widely enough, they cease to be marauders, become founders of a new moral order. "Man is the measure of all things," said Protagoras, "of things that are, that they are, and of things that are not, that they are not." Rules of just conduct swear allegiance to success.

"There is no history of mankind," writes Karl Popper, "there is only an indefinite number of histories of all kinds of aspects of human life. And one of these is the history of political power. This is elevated into the history of the world. But this, I hold, is an offense against every decent conception of mankind. It is hardly better than to treat the history of embezzlement or of robbery or of poisoning as the history of mankind. *For the history of power politics is nothing but the history of international crime and mass murder* (including, it is true, some of the attempts to suppress them). This history is taught in schools, and some of the greatest criminals are extolled as its heroes." [1] History has no meaning, he asserts, but we can interpret it, "with an eye to those problems of power politics whose solution we choose to attempt in our time. We can interpret the history of power politics from the point of view of our fight for the open society, for a rule of reason, for justice, freedom, equality, and for the control of international crime. Although history has no ends, we can impose these ends of ours upon it; and *although history has no meaning, we can give it a meaning.*" [2]

These words have a noble ring but a hollow echo. Will future generations, looking back on *their* history which is *our* present, find in it the meaning we have so given it?

Will they, for example, find the meaning of World War II to consist of the struggle of the Western democracies to maintain an open society? Perhaps. But only if they write from the point of view of that open society—that is, only if our values should prevail, if they retain that *power* of which Popper is so contemptuous. If, however, another Hitler should succeed in those aims in which the first one failed, the historians who would write from the point of view of the values then obtaining might say—in Popper's exact words, forcing them down his throat, as it were—that history has only that meaning which we give to it with our efforts, and that the meaning of World War II is to be found in those gallant, though temporarily unsuccessful, efforts of the Nazis to establish a world hegemony which would at last make possible a rule of law and order. The attempt to *give* meaning to history, therefore, leads straight back to that political power which, as Popper sees it, is but the record of international brigandage.

We cannot create morality anew, can never start with a clean slate. Were we to compose a code of conduct and find it valid, it would but put in writing a preexisting morality. Nor can law create morality; for laws are themselves judged by a morality which is beyond any law. When we speak of an "unjust law" we mean that it conflicts with a moral principle which was well established before the law was written, before the state which enacts that law even came into existence. An unjust law can make immoral behavior legal but cannot make it moral.

Nor can morality be created by reason. "Standards of morality and justice," writes Christian Bay, "are what Hume called 'artifacts'; they are neither divinely ordained, nor an integral part of original human nature, nor revealed by pure reason. They are an outcome of the practical experience of mankind, and the sole consideration in the slow test of time is the utility each moral rule can demonstrate toward promoting human welfare." [3] Moral law "is not only much older than legislation," writes Hayek, "or even an organized state: the whole authority of the legislator and of the state derives from pre-existing conceptions of justice, and no system of articulated law can be applied except within a framework of generally recognized but often unarticulated rules of justice." [4]

Always there is conflict of interest; classes contend, forces disrupt. No group is of a piece, and if it is to survive—if traffic is to flow through intersections, utilities to provide service, people to be fed and clothed, children schooled—if these necessary processes are to continue, order must be maintained.

Order derives from force and from authority, which parallel jungle and community. In the most pacific community one finds force: every town has a sheriff, every country an army. And the most violent community retains elements of authority. One increases at the expense of the other: the greater the authority of government the less force it needs to govern; the less the authority, the more force. Insofar as a group is a community its order derives from authority; insofar as it is a jungle, from force.

Order may be maintained by either. Prisoners may strain to tear each other to pieces yet proceed with perfect discipline through designated routines, the source of that order being armed guards. In any community the degree to which order is maintained by force measures the degree to which that community is in danger of becoming a jungle. All was orderly in Czechoslovakia in the summer of 1968, but the newly installed government lacked authority; order derived from Russian soldiers, Russian tanks.

Authority derives from principle, force issues from the muzzle of a gun. Authority in a leader depends upon the degree to which he embodies principles of basic value to the community, principles transcending the interest of any group or class. When President Kennedy addressed the nation on the evening of the Bay of Pigs he embodied those American ideals, one of which is honesty, with which he had identified himself so effectively in his inaugural address; and he spoke with the authority of our shared allegiance to those ideals. When he told us that the United States, though in sympathy with the Cuban revolt, had no part in it, we believed him. When in subsequent weeks it transpired that he had lied, his authority was diminished. It had been in the immediate interest of his government that its initiative in this invasion not be known, and he placed that interest above honesty. To that extent he represented partisan interest rather than principle, and to that extent he lost authority. When ends justify means we come, however holy the ends, to force; when means are made to conform to ends, even at the risk of our not achieving the ends, we gain authority. In our time authority declines; flags are hauled down and trampled; institutions of government are derided; rulers are nervous, keep one hand on a gun.

As authority is lost, effectiveness may yet be maintained, may even increase. Advertising controls buying by telling lies—by telling them as widely and prominently as possible, and in the most beguiling way. It is without authority, but effective. Mussolini got the trains running on time, Germany prepared for war with breathtaking speed, and Russia accomplished prodigiously under tyranny. If effectiveness is the criterion we will not necessarily choose authority; advocates of force cite many triumphs of efficiency.

In one decade the crime rate in America has doubled. Not because the force available to prevent it has been reduced; for such force has everywhere been increased. Force prevents crime when the police car cruises within sight, whereas authority, when it is present in the social order, installs itself in some measure in the heart of each individual. All of us, potentially, are criminals; we do not become actual criminals because this social authority operates within us. As this authority, embodied in political leaders and in social and governmental institutions, diminishes, the balance within us is upset; and some of us, who required that external reinforcement of internal prohibition for moral restraint, begin to act on impulse, to serve our own interest, to be accountable to no one.

As we have lost authority more rapidly than we have been willing to increase force, crime increases and order is progressively lost. If we greatly increase force—engage more police, suspend civil rights, execute felons on sight —we may regain order, perhaps such order as prevailed in Germany in 1938, even as the erosion of authority continues. Is this the way we must go?

Or can we yet find some way to regain authority in social life? Since authority rests on principle, such a quest is moral, places the good above the expedient, may require us to choose a course of action we believe right over one which seems better suited to national security.

Consequences of acts may now be known more extensively and much more rapidly than ever before. Sometimes they can be known instantaneously, sometimes even prior to the acts from which they follow. Computers working with votes cast in the morning predict election results in time to affect votes still to be cast in the afternoon, may bring it about that one does not bother going to the polls, or, arriving there, writes in Tarzan for President.

Marshall McLuhan argues that lying has become necessary because technology has made it so easy and so useful. "It is the instant consequences of electrically moved information," he says, "that makes necessary a deliberate artistic aim in the placing and management of news. In diplomacy the same electric speed causes the decisions to be announced before they are made in order to ascertain the varying responses that might occur when such decisions actually are made." If the idea of lying offends us, he suggests we revise our standards rather than abstain from lying.[5]

In a small and isolated culture principles may seem coherent and homogeneous. In the increasingly worldwide culture, electronically mediated, conflict of principle is everywhere. All principles are seen then as relative and we despair of principle as a guide. At the same time, knowing more and more about the probable consequences of our contemplated acts, we more and more are tempted to act in accord with desired outcome rather than with principle.[6] But beyond the short- and middle-range consequences of our actions which we foresee lie the remote and unforeseeable. However long the reach of knowing, something remains beyond that reach. No gain in vision enables the seeing eye to see itself, nor the mind that forsakes principle for consequence to foresee the consequences of its having become that sort of mind.

There is no morality without principle, but no principle guarantees goodness. The noblest adherence to virtue is compatible with monstrous evil. Saint-Just, archangel of the French Revolution, wanted nothing for himself, but freedom and equality and brotherhood for all. He pursued these ends with purity of heart, with relentless virtue and strictest adherence to principle—and sent thousands to the guillotine.[7]

Morality is a wall. On it is written: Whatever passion impel you, whatever goal you pursue, beyond this limit you may not go; and no loving, however great, not even the willingness to lay down your life for him whose rights you would violate, will gain for you the right to trespass.

Wherever a moral order obtains, freedom is secured, not by one's strength to resist the strong, but by the authority of limits installed in the hearts of those who have the strength to enslave.

Slave morality, says Nietzsche, is always puling about freedom because slaves, unable to achieve freedom by force, appeal to principle. The morality so damned is the only morality there is, for what Nietzsche calls master morality is not morality at all, but force. The freedom of the strong, maintained by strength, is not a moral good but a good of arms; and however good the tyrant, if he recognizes no law beyond his will, his goodness is not moral.

VI

We and They

BOTH morality and goodness depend upon our taking the part of the other. How far afield can we go and still see ourselves in another?

Three men run from a bank with bags of money; police pursue, firing. One of the bandits is hit, falls to the ground. His comrades turn back, one picks him up while the third holds off police with opposing gunfire; the three escape together. Here is morality: the three men form a community within which, by empathy, they take the part of the other. When they say good they mean good for the gang, for all three of them. We huddle in a recessed doorway, see outlaws committing a crime, observe no moral order. Yet every social unit, including this one, has two faces: looking inward to its constituent members, it is a whole; looking outward to the larger neighborhood, it is a part. Considered as a whole, this one is a moral order, its members identifying with the social entity comprised of their several lives; considered as part of a larger neighborhood, it is an outlaw.

If we acknowledge their morality at all, we see it as pathetically limited. They should be able, we feel, to live in a community of greater scope, to take the part not only of each other, but of tellers in the bank, of the police who may be killed, of ourselves the endangered passers-by. And this view, we believe, is not subjective and arbitrary, but objective, capable of demonstration; for the clothes they wear are sewn by others, their bread is baked by others, other men have made the car in which they escape, will provide medical care when they are wounded.

Yet if we can bring ourselves to see the morality, however limited, in that going back for a fallen comrade, we can trace its development, follow its course until it reaches ourselves, we who write and read about morality, we who in reference to some even larger neighborhood may still be acting as an outlaw gang, and by tracing out this course may be able to envision its possible future extension—only possible, for no law guarantees moral progress.

We say "we" and we say "they." "We" are those who comprise the group to which the "I" belongs; "they" belong to some other group. We and they exchange goods, form alliances, even intermarry; but when trouble comes, and it always does, we remember that we are we and they are they. We fall upon them and destroy them—or they destroy us. But neither we nor they are destroyed completely. Always there are survivors, the captives, the slaves, who are taken over, bleeding and sullen, to be exploited by the victors, in the course of which they are assimilated and so become, eventually, part of the victors "we." So groups grow larger.

Once the "we" was a band of hunting men with stone weapons, followed after by a straggle of women and children quarreling over scraps from the kill. Once it was a handful of nomads in animal skins herding their flocks. Thousands of years later it was an agricultural village, each family tilling its own field with ard plow and stone hoe. In the cities of Sumer the "we" became a civilization, diversified in class and function, some of the people producing the food for all. Then we could afford priests and warriors. "Our" warriors attacked "their" warriors and defeated them, and "they" became part of our "we"; and "we" then became a federation. Lugalzaggisi, King of Umma, united the cities of Sumer. Federation attacked federation, victor absorbed vanquished, and presently Sargon of Akkad ruled an empire. And lost it. And Hammurabi of Babylon won it back again. Then he—and we and they —were in turn swallowed up by the even greater empire of Darius the Great. So the "we" grows larger, more organized, the division of labor ever more complex. Millennia pass, and now our hierarchies of specialization culminate in very special priests, very special warriors, and most unusual weapons.

The extent of the "we" is the extent of brotherhood. The genealogy of love is conquest. My black brother today was my black slave yesterday. Now he and I are "we"—though, as he tirelessly reminds me, that "we-ness" is less than perfect. Patience, brother. The story isn't over, and tomorrow you and I, who now are "we," may both be vanquished, and those of us who survive become slaves to some other "they," and so eventually part of their then larger "we."

Dare we look back over the way we have come and see that it was our wandering rape and pillage that led to our widening love and brotherhood? Can it be that caring follows after the bullet from the muzzle of a gun?

A collective entity without power breaks apart in times of crisis. We are devoted to mankind as a universal brotherhood, but "mankind" has no organization with which to transform devotion into power, so in times of war this devotion is pirated by the state. For the state *is* organized, has structured means of translating patriotism into power, and in times of crisis wants ever more power, can never get enough, lays claim not only to the freely and spontaneously offered loyalty to which it is entitled, but also, representing its national purpose as the universal aim of man, to the loyalty which its people hold for mankind.[1]

Statesmen are concerned with states, their identifications go to the border. Further extensions are tenuous and in critical times are abruptly dropped. Statesmen defend and preserve the state, as if its special quality, its spirit, institutions, customs, even its balance of rich and poor, exploiter and exploited, should be preserved, should sail on forever a sovereign ship into the ocean of future time.

Those of us who are not statesmen are free to have larger concerns. We are humanists, we criticize the defensive stance of nations, see it as a squabbling among neighbors who comprise one community united by interconnecting networks of goods, services, ideas. Our identifications do not pause at national borders but reach out to all mankind. "A human pattern," writes Lewis Mumford, "a human measure, a human tempo, above all a human goal must transform the activities and processes of technics." [2]

The vision which we consider so limited in the defense of nations is, in this humanist view, paralleled one level up in the defense of mankind. By what reason can a stand made here be judged less arbitrary? What basis for such a claim? The same basis, it would seem, and no more, as that of some prescient fish a billion years back drawing the line at gills, identifying with all the fish in the sea but holding that life should not move on to lungs, to mammals, to pica-resque adventures on land. How could his fellow fish have proved him wrong? How can we? How, likewise, can we know that the welfare and the preservation of mankind is desirable? Perhaps man should evolve into something different. How can we know, indeed, that we should not perish in order that some other form of life might flourish?

If humanism refers to human nature it is a questionable standard of excellence; for our nature, with all its glories and triumphs of spirit, is marked by viciousness. If, on the other hand, humanism refers selectively to the loving, the creative, and the nurturing aspects of our nature, the doctrine is misnamed; for in that event it looks forward not to the preservation of man but to his evolution into something different from any humanity yet known to this planet.

After us, it is grimly said, come the roaches. Well? And why would that be bad? Because, it might be argued, if we are to have values at all we must make a stand somewhere, and the most logical place to locate the good is in that evolutionary progression toward greater awareness of which man occupies the furthermost point. Yet even so, such a temporary setback to this process as the disappearance of man on earth might conceivably serve a later and greater advance.

Birds, reptiles, insects have come to the end of the road, have achieved such physical specialization that they can no longer make significant change in response to an altered environment, in a changed world would perish. Even the apes have reached such a point, so adapted to tree life that were trees to disappear the apes would go too. The genius of man—which makes him lord and possessor of the universe, we are told—is to have avoided this dead end. So we survived the ice age, the black death, and so we will survive the end of trees, or anything else. Because we *think*, adapt by thought rather than physical configuration, evolve culturally. But specialization cannot see itself. The special feature of man is indeed the ability to think and to communicate; and one of the things we can think is whence comes the energy of the sun, and one of the things we have learned is how to create it. And another thing we can think is: "Better destroy the Russians because they are preparing to destroy us." And the ability to think such things and persuasively to communicate them may prove, like the giantism of the dinosaur, the fatal specialization of man.

Where draw the line? Where find a limit for identification that escapes the arbitrary? That's too much to ask, we'd settle for less: Where find a limit that diminishes even a bit the arbitrariness of the lines we draw, the limits we set? Is there any principle to guide the trajectory of identifications, to bring them to rest at a point which, though still fallibly arrived at, is less arbitrary than any other point?

Though we may never know how far community *should* extend, we know a limit beyond which it cannot go. In the tenth century there could have been no community of Incas and Europeans, for these peoples were unaware of each other's existence, had not the possibility of contact, interaction, understanding. Likewise we cannot now, even if we should so wish, act in the interest of unknown forms of life in unknown regions of the universe.

The rational extent of community is the range of cooperation. If a man in a grass hut in Bombay prints a piece of silk with brilliant dyes, and if after many intermediate steps it comes about that I buy that silk and wear it around my neck, then I and that Indian are related by cooperative endeavor, and it must be my concern that he receives something in exchange, and, if he and his family are starving, their fate must lie on my heart, impel me to reach him with help without being halted at a border by considerations of national interest.

The growth of awareness and cooperation and relatedness proceeds ever outward, embraces greater variety, covers greater distance, longer time. This is the line of evolutionary development: knowledge and awareness expand. As the world that we know is larger than that of an earthworm, so the world of creatures yet to come may exceed our own. The limits of identification should correspond to the limits of understanding. They can be no greater; perhaps we should not permit them to be less. The understanding of man need not pause at national boundaries, reaches on to all mankind, and perhaps a bit further—to banyan trees, to the great blue whale, and the wild honking goose.

The organization of mankind into ever larger aggregates is the basis for gains both in goodness and in evil. Wherever we find moral progress, if we reduce it to the conditions from which it developed, we find the coalescence of peoples. And wherever we find growth of evil, an expanding magnitude of cruelty and destruction—and we find it everywhere—and reduce it to the conditions from which it arose, we arrive at the same process.

What kind of Hegelian joke have we concocted? Good and evil comprised of the same ingredients, derived from the same recipe! It's true. And this is reason neither for despair nor for optimism, means only that the issue is open and uncertain. We may arrive at a world state or at no world at all.[3] We may, if we must, so conceive the world that everything becomes rational. Hegel and Marx so conceived it; indeed all of us in the Modern Age, with our vision of mechanism, have imposed reason on the weather of our days. But we can't have it for nothing, so had better be honest about the price: make everything rational and lose freedom; or, secure freedom and lose hope of justifying history as the working out of a rational plan.[4]

Theodicy is theidiocy, and in our time theodicists have become theoddest of us all.

VII

Jungle and Community

HUMAN society may be seen with equal ease as a jungle or as a community. Those who see a jungle call themselves realists. They observe that our pieties are masks for selfishness, that hard on the heels of the missionary comes the soldier, that as we go about the world proclaiming love and brotherhood we do business as usual, and that the usual business of mankind is exploitation and murder. Ask any U.S. Marine about the proud motto of his Corps, *Semper Fidelis*, and you will find he understands Latin perfectly: "Fuck you, buddy! I've got mine, now you get yours." Anyone who doesn't accept this translation is a "sucker." Such realists see community, also, but see it as a false front, regard those who take it seriously as wishful thinkers. They make a cogent case; for in even the best-ordered society there is so much of dog-eat-dog that over Wall Street, over the *Bourse*, over the temples and palaces of the world, arises the very smell of jungle.

Those who see community feel that it is they who are the realists, that those who see only jungle are blind to the facts of community, and so inadvertently augment the quality of jungle. They see jungle, too, but see through it, they feel, to the underlying realities of social life. And they, too, make a cogent case; for in even the most disturbed and violent society there is still much of cooperation and mutual concern, and it is a matter of common record that many a Marine has turned back into a rain of machine-gun fire to pick up a wounded comrade.

Both are true; neither view can exclude the other. In the behavior of ants we may believe we see pure community, and in a pack of wolves crazed by blood and turning upon each other, we may recognize pure jungle; but such unmixed states, if they exist at all, must be rare. Wherever we look at human affairs we see both.

They contend with each other, and either may increase at the expense of the other. In Germany in the first months of 1945 the jungle all but obliterates community. For years it has been a land of murder, of locked trains carrying millions to factories of death. Now as the German armies begin to collapse, as Allied bombing destroys German cities and industries at an ever-increasing pace, a further and more rapid breakdown of community occurs. German people turn upon each other in frenzied destruction. The People's Court makes a mockery of justice, a circus for the amusement of the masses, as even the relatives and friends of the July 1944 conspirators are strangled in public ceremony.[1] Soldiers are warned that even the families of deserters will be shot, people who hoard food are shot, people who spread rumors are shot, people found on roadways without papers are shot, those who change address without notifying the proper authorities are shot. Between the shifting boundaries of the two armies bands of slaves who have broken free roam about ravaging deserted townships, taking vengeance on any civilians who remain.[2] The structure of civilization falls away into rubble.

Yet even in this extremity of social disorganization there

remained aspects of community: some telephone exchanges still worked, some public utilities provided service, some army units functioned as groups, some factories produced goods.

One evening in 1942 we stand at a window high in the Empire State Building. It is bright moonlight, but there is no other light anywhere; we are at war and the city is testing its defenses. The immense towers of Manhattan loom like ghostly ruins of a megalithic culture, and we wonder if this is a vision of things to come. Will these towers stand here one day deserted, headstones in the graveyard of one more civilization? Only yesterday it seemed utterly secure. "The world has become a jungle," one of us says. "On the contrary," says another, "we have never been so truly a community."

The one who sees jungle is thinking of the behavior of nation with nation, of tanks rolling into Poland, of German planes pulverizing Rotterdam, of the Russian attack on Finland, of Italy jumping in at the last moment on a prostrate France, of the attack on Pearl Harbor as Japanese emissaries in Washington create an illusion of good will. The one who sees community is considering only the United States, perceiving within this country a deeper sense of unity, of shared purpose, of willingness to sacrifice. Both are true: at one level we have become more truly a community, at the other more truly a jungle.

Societies are not congeries of individuals, but hierarchies of social units. Individuals live in families, families in neighborhoods; neighborhoods form cities; nations group together into alliances. At each level the subordinate units are organized into a community by whatever rules obtain at that level; and at each level such rules may become stronger with some gain in community, or may break down, leaving component units to deal with each other as in a jungle. In 1942 the community within nations was strong; but such community as had existed between the two alliances of nations was utterly lost, and they were destroying each other.

Since we no longer believe the course of man's future to have been antecedently determined by God, or by the deterministic operation of natural laws, what we envision, what we intend, what we strive for, will make a difference in that as yet undetermined future that is to come. We want a world which will be more of a community, less of a jungle. We must inquire, therefore, what are the sources of community, how may they be nurtured.

Designations of good and evil imply favorable or unfavorable consequences, not to an individual, but to a community. When the referent of value is no more than oneself, opportunism is defined; and when we say of such a person, "He is a law unto himself," or "The good is simply what is good for him," we are figuratively extending the terms of morality to a jungle where morality does not exist. Even when we act in utter isolation, if the action is moral it bears witness to our membership in some community, real or imagined. Designations of good and evil upon which there is general agreement are expressed in law. Law, therefore, though lagging behind, attempts to secure good for a community and to prevent evil—as good and evil are perceived by that community.

As we walk about our neighborhood we feel ourselves in a community. The jungle is not altogether absent, may spring out at us at any moment, in our times is more and more in evidence; yet still in large measure we expect community, accord community, and find community. We expect others to stop at red lights, to observe property rights, to honor contracts, and we do not rebel at having to do so ourselves. We share a willingness to be subject to a law which we believe protects the general good.

In times of peace we find community, also, in the behavior of nations. Embassies, consulates, trade agreements, the interchange of science, music, literature, all bear witness. But at this level of social organization community is fragile, frequently breaks down; frontiers close to peaceful traffic, are violated by tanks and planes.

This rather more vulnerable community of nations derives from the rather smaller willingness of nations to be subject to law. As individuals, claiming no sovereignty, willingly subject to law, we live in a relatively secure community; as sovereign nations, subject to no law, we live in a community which at times disappears, leaving only jungle.

No Constitution guarantees freedom, nor Bill of Rights, nor Writ of Habeas Corpus; all may be suspended in time of crisis, as they were for Americans of Japanese ancestry during World War II. Freedom does not rest secure upon law, but requires a living tradition. "Institutions are always ambivalent," writes Karl Popper, "in the sense that, in the absence of a strong tradition, they also may serve the opposite purpose to the one intended. . . . All laws, being universal principles, have to be interpreted in order to be applied; and an interpretation needs some principles of concrete practice, which can be supplied only by a living tradition. . . . Among the traditions we must count as the most important is what we may call the 'moral framework' . . . of a society. This incorporates the society's traditional sense of justice or fairness, or the degree of moral sensitivity it has reached. This moral framework serves as the basis which makes it possible to reach a fair or equitable compromise between conflicting interests where this is necessary. It is, of course, itself not unchangeable, but it changes comparatively slowly. Nothing is more dangerous than the destruction of this traditional framework." [3]

Nature is amoral, morality is unnatural. Our lives are meridian to these poles. Love and hate, nurture and murder, they spring from our nature with equal authenticity. But nature no longer leads, authenticates nothing. We say love is right and hate is wrong, and so leave nature, struggle toward a moral order.

We live in a jungle and we live in a community. He who would assert either to the exclusion of the other will find ample evidence for the realm of his choice. We know both, but assert that the way of love, of community, of caring for one's neighbor is right, and that the way of the jungle is wrong. No one leads us. We stand aside from nature, seek a god in the image of what we arbitrarily designate as our better selves.

VIII

Hierarchy

THERE is much agreement in our judgment of the good and evil of individual behavior, little agreement in our judgments of the good and evil of national behavior. We can judge a defeated enemy: Germany's murder of the Jews was evil. But when we consider ourselves and our allies we are unsure. Nations act and their actions affect millions of people, entail much killing, and we cannot agree about the right and wrong of what they do. The destruction of Hiroshima, of Dresden; Holland fighting the invading Germans, Denmark not fighting; the American intervention in Korea, the Israeli Six-Day War—many of us feel competent to judge these actions, but there is no consensus; and how are we to judge wrong those who judge differently?

The more we accept the authority of law, the greater our agreement about right and wrong; the less we accept the authority of law, the less the agreement. As individuals we acknowledge law that transcends self-interest; as nations we are unwilling to subordinate national interest to larger principles.

Finding no criterion by which we may uniformly arrive at judgments of collective responsibility, some of us despair of collective morality and hold that the unit of moral action, and hence of responsibility, is always an individual. We cannot find it in anything *less* than an individual, they would remind us, and we should not expect it in anything *more* than an individual. The prisoner is charged with murder and we must judge him as a whole man, may not find his hand guilty and his eye innocent. Likewise we may not find guilty or innocent the Hell's Angels to which he belongs, nor the Teamsters' Union, nor the Chattanooga Street Poker Club. According to this view, we may begin by indicting the Hell's Angels but must end by finding guilty one or more individuals. Likewise, in our conflict with Nazi Germany we begin by indicting a nation but will arrive eventually, if we are conscientious and careful, as indeed we were at Nuremberg, at a few men, the rulers. It is they who hold authority to determine the nation's action; if that action is evil these men are responsible. Where authority is divided, responsibility is proportional to authority. When a country is ruled by a despot he alone is responsible. By this view Göring and Hitler are accountable for the bombing of Rotterdam, but not the men who built the planes.

Those who oppose this view hold that the unit of moral action may be either an individual or a collective, that the morality of the one bears no necessary relation to that of the other, that either or both, as circumstances may indicate, may reasonably be indicted and justly be found guilty or innocent. They would warn us that collective responsibility for collective action has in our time acquired an urgency altogether new; for whereas in the past we have always been prepared, on finding collective guilt, to find individual guilt also, our technology has so separated us from the consequences of our acts that we now may have collective guilt without any individual guilt. The tendency of civilization is not to eliminate destructiveness nor even diminish it, but to remove it. Tooth to hand to stone to blade to bullet to bomb—so man estranges himself from his victim. Our fate falls now from the touch of a finger in a cave of ice.[1]

"A person is a complex whole having a single life," writes Bertrand Russell; "can there be a super-person, composed of persons as the body is composed of organs, and having a single life which is not the sum of the lives of the component persons? If there can be such a super-person . . . then the State may be such a being, and it may be as superior to ourselves as the whole body is to the eye. But if we think this super-person a mere metaphysical monstrosity, then we shall say that the intrinsic value of a community is derived from that of its members, and that the State is a means, not an end."[2]

Russell here begs rather than argues the question, first designating the larger whole as a super-person, then asking if we can recognize the state as such. For there is no reason to expect that entity the parts of which are human individuals to resemble a person, no more than the parts of a person should resemble a person. We would get nowhere in understanding the eye if we conceived of it as a subperson. In most contexts the eye is a part, yet in some a whole; for it can be kept alive outside the body, can be transplanted, can be conveyed in a will. In no case, however, does it resemble a person. In most contexts, likewise, the individual is a whole, yet in some must be seen as part of a state. The fact that a state is not a super-person does not diminish it as an entity nor deprive it of reality, indicates only that it must be recognized as something in itself, of its own kind, as different from individual persons as is a person from component organs. A state is not a congeries of individuals wandering about in physical proximity, but an organized association of individuals, an entity with a life of its own different in quality and pattern from the life of a person. To it value may accrue; a course of action may be *good* for the state even though destructive of certain individuals within that state, as an operation for cancer may be good for the individual though it entail the removal, and hence the death, of related organs, even organs not directly involved in the cancer.

Those who believe that a nation may justly be indicted for wrongdoing would remind us that the conditions for morality are insight and action, and that nations as well as individuals possess these attributes. Germany under Hitler embarked on an evil course, is therefore guilty as a nation. Insight into good and evil, by this view, is possessed not only by individual Germans but at a higher level by the collective, a supra-individual awareness comprised of innumerable individual contributions which do not, however, remain a summation but become a cohesive structure of awareness. The nation, likewise, has a freedom to act that is superordinate to the freedom of action of any individual, not excluding such powerful individuals as Hitler. Never could we reconstruct the action of German armies by examining the lives, feelings, purposes of individual soldiers, however numerous. It is the state that must be examined if we are to understand the movement of armies or the building of extermination camps. And in exactly the same way that such actions must be ascribed not to individuals but to the nation, so must the awareness, the insight, the knowledge of good and evil, be ascribed to the nation. With the same logic.

The issue, as C. E. Ayres makes clear, is between universes of discourse, or levels of generalization, not realms of being. "Any given substance such, for example, as table salt may be said to be composed entirely of electrons, protons, neutrons, etc.; or it may be said to be composed entirely of atoms; or it may be said to be composed entirely of molecules; or it may be said to be composed entirely of crystals. None of these propositions invalidates any other. None can be substituted for any other, and especially not in part. Thus it would be a complete misrepresentation of both the physics and the chemistry of sodium chloride to say that this substance consists in part of electrons and in part of molecules. Insofar as molecular structure is concerned at all, it is co-extensive with the salt. A given quantity of salt may be partly crystalline and partly in solution in water, but it may not be partly crystalline and partly atomic." [3]

In exactly the same sense, human behavior is wholly individual and wholly social. The relationship is one of complete alternativity; and the relationship of the individual cell to the organism offers an exact analogy. "All human activities are the sum of the acts of individual men. This is the level of generalization on which ordinary human affairs are conducted and for which the question is all-important, 'Who has acted how, and why?' The functions, factors, and forces into which culture is resolved . . . do not 'act' as men act; but they do constitute a causal nexus the analysis of which is the problem of the social sciences, and in this analysis of social causes and effects the acts of individual men are not at issue." [4]

Who is responsible for collective wrongdoing? Who should be punished for My-Lai? Shall we say that the right and wrong of conduct necessarily refer to human beings in their separateness, to persons who are guided, or who decline to be guided, by conscience? If so we will seek out those persons who committed the crime and those persons who had authority to stop it and did not. Or shall we say that responsibility for group action must be borne by the group as a whole, cannot be meted out to individuals in quantities proportional to the directness of their involvement?

We cannot, and need not, choose between these points of view. They do not contend, but refer to entities existing at different levels. The two levels are equally real. The responsibility for My-Lai is not *partly* individual and *partly* social; it is altogether individual and altogether social. One does not cease to be an individual, with individual insight and freedom and authority, just because one is engaged in group action. The collective guilt of the army or of the nation does not render innocent the soldier who shoots down unarmed women and children, whether or not he is so ordered. But neither does the guilt of individuals exonerate the group. Collective action depends upon collective effort and collective will; marauding armies abroad depend upon support from home; and responsibility for what these armies do must be borne by the nation.

England judges the actions of Nazi Germany as evil, decides that the *right* action for England is war. This decision must be judged—if it can be judged at all—in the context of rules of just conduct governing the behavior of nation with nation. If, being so judged, it is found to be just, and if the proper pursuit of this war requires the destruction of cities—including women and children, the aged and the ill, even those who oppose German policy, babes in arm who have neither insight nor freedom— then such destruction is *right*, for the reason that German guilt is collective. England acts as a moral entity against Germany as a moral entity: each *knows* the nature of its action, each has freedom, each is accountable. That the innocent perish is a pity, but is irrelevant to the moral problem, is indeed comparable to the observation that when the murderer is executed, his eye and his ear perish too. Though we may not ascribe guilt to these parts, neither may we ascribe innocence: neither is applicable, both are irrelevant. The moral agent in the case of individual crime is the whole man who plans and executes the murder; the moral agent in the case of war is the whole nation. By this view, England becomes guilty of *wrong* action in its conduct of a just war only if it destroys cities the destruction of which is unnecessary to the proper pursuit of the war.

But then who is to say, in war, what destruction is necessary? The victor rules. Dresden and Hiroshima were necessary; Rotterdam and Coventry were crimes against humanity.[5]

If the behavior of men is not limited by principle it will be dominated by self-interest, and life will be a jungle. The interest of one conflicts with the interest of another; and without shared allegiance to principles superordinate to the conflicting selves, issues will be settled by force. Likewise, if nothing limits national interest in the behavior of nations, nations will live together as in a jungle. Within any one nation people may have achieved community, ordering their lives within the limits described by shared ideals and principles; yet these same people, acting collectively, may recognize the interest of only their own nation and defer only to force.

Human life exists at many levels. The individual level is of unique interest, clarity, and fixation, and is for each of us unforgettable; but no level is ultimate, and no level may in all instances take priority over the others. Each unit faces two ways: as a whole it looks inward to constituent parts; as a part it looks outward to the superordinate whole of which it is itself a part.[6] A family may have achieved community among its members, yet may act toward other families as in a jungle, may provision its bomb shelter not only with food and water but with guns with which to fend off, when the missiles come, the then desperate family from across the street who built no shelter, who will come begging, will beat upon the door. At whatever level the life of man is being considered, a moral order obtains only if the units existing at that level limit their behavior according to principles transcending the interest of those individual units.

Arthur Koestler, though he has examined hierarchic structure in great detail, remains fixed at the individual level, regards group aggression as reducible to individual determinants. He points out that self-assertive and self-transcending tendencies, in varying proportions, characterize every human impulse; that the self-assertive tendency reflects the claim of an individual to be an independent whole, whereas the self-transcending tendency reflects the individual's need to be part of a larger whole; and he asserts that mankind's present predicament is to be ascribed to his self-transcending tendency. "The point I shall try to make," he writes, "is that selfishness is not the primary culprit; and that appeals to man's better nature were bound to be ineffectual because the main danger lies precisely in what we are wont to call his 'better nature.' In other words, I would like to suggest that the *integrative tendencies of the individual are incomparably more dangerous than his self-assertive tendencies.*" [7] Referring to religious, patriotic, and ideological wars, all "fought with the same self-immolating loyalty and fervor," [8] he says that the "ravages caused by the excess of individual self-assertion are . . . relatively small compared to those which result from misplaced devotion." [9] Yet the logic of his position would require him to say, rather, that the ravages caused by the excess of individual self-assertion are relatively small compared to the ravages caused by an excess of group self-assertion. "It *was not individual aggression which got out of hand,*" he writes, "*but devotion to the narrow social group with which the individual identified himself to the hostile exclusion of all other groups.*" [10] True, it was not individual aggression which got out of hand, but it was not individual devotion either. To lay the responsibility for group aggression upon that devotion of individuals without which the group could not exist is like blaming the fidelity of the trigger-finger for the crime of the gunman. We cannot reduce the Inquisition to the piety of individual priests, nor understand the Soviet purges by interviewing Volga boatmen. The phenomena are lost at that level and cannot be reconstructed by the summation of however many individual elements. To understand the Inquisition we must study the church and the society to which it ministered; to understand the purges we must study the Soviet state.

At times Koestler seems to grasp this point: "*The self-assertive behavior of the group is based on the self-transcending behavior of its members.*" But then he loses it two pages later, saying, "War is a ritual, a deadly ritual, *not the result of aggressive self-assertion, but of self-transcending identification*," [11] when the logic of hierarchic structure and of his own argument require him to say, rather, that war is not the result of aggressive self-assertion, but of aggressive group-assertion.

Thirty-five years earlier, Reinhold Niebuhr had examined the same issue and arrived at the same conclusion. There is an ethical paradox in patriotism, he wrote in 1932; it "transmutes individual unselfishness into national egoism. . . . The unqualified character of this devotion is the very basis of the nation's power and of the freedom to use the power without moral restraint. Thus the unselfishness of individuals makes for the selfishness of nations. That is why the hope of solving the larger social problems of mankind, merely by extending the social sympathies of individuals, is so vain. Altruistic passion is sluiced into the reservoirs of nationalism with great ease, and is made to flow beyond them with great difficulty. What lies beyond the nation, the community of mankind, is too vague to inspire devotion." [12]

Koestler, having failed at the crucial point to specify the social level of the hierarchic order, proceeds to deal with the destructive phenomena of social life by scrutinizing the individual brain and its evolutionary development, and to hope that we may soon be able, by the mass use of new drugs, to achieve "an artificially simulated, adaptive mutation." [13] Yet his own argument has made it abundantly clear that we can never understand social action by examining individual attributes, and that to look for the causes of war in the anatomy of the individual brain is like trying to understand courage by dissecting muscles. We will find the causes of war by examining the entities which wage war. In the modern world this is the national state. The urgent predicament of mankind is not individual but social, and our greatest danger lies in actions which only the state can take. It is true, as Niebuhr said, that we cannot solve the "larger social problems of mankind merely by extending the social sympathies of individuals," but from this we must conclude that we should seek ways, rather, of extending the social sympathies of societies. The issues we most need to control lie within the power and the provenance of the state, and it is the state—its configuration, its institutions, its traditions, its conduits of power, its modes of decision and action, above all its demand for sovereignty—that we must understand and change.

A moral order at the level of individual behavior is enforced by the social entity of which individuals are constituent, but that social entity is not itself within that moral order nor subject to the limits which that order defines. The demand for money accompanied by threat of coercion, coming from an individual, is a holdup; from the state, taxation.

The relation of the collective to its constituents is positive and directive: it is responsible for preserving and supervising the moral order which governs the relations between individuals, and in this capacity undertakes to regulate, to control, and occasionally to coerce. It is responsible also for achieving certain goods: it does not request, it demands that individuals pay taxes to support schools, submit to vaccination to prevent epidemics, bear arms to defend the group against aggression.

A moral order governing the relations of nations to each other, should it ever come about, would be analogous, would be to the several nations as these nations are to their own elements.

IX

The Meta-Conscious

WE are more than we know. Freud taught us this so thoroughly that no one any longer can doubt it. We are only just now, however, beginning to learn, further, that we are more than we *can* know. More than we can know *ever*. More both as individuals and as groups. More in principle, and so must live with an ignorance which is irreducible by any gain in knowing. More, not in the sense of unconscious or repressed, of something pushed aside or passed by, but in the opposite sense of something which goes before us, draws us forward, determines the configurations of our awareness but which is itself beyond the reach of awareness.

We have to *be* something before we can *know* anything. And when we have become something that can know something, the something we can know is less than the something we have become. When the knower studies knowing, the most he can learn is less than he knows. A rule of mental operation is not to be created by design, is not something that mind *does*, but something that mind *is*, one of the processes that constitute mind, and so determines those other things that mind can create. Rules of just conduct are not something we make, but something within us, already made, which we discover.

No computer can design another computer as complex as itself. If we imagine a succession of computers, each generation designed by its precursor, we see a degenerating sequence—electronic circuits becoming mechanical, thinking machines becoming adding machines, tasks assignable becoming ever more simple, keys sounding ever more faintly, then sounding not at all. Yet each generation of mankind creates another generation as complex as itself. And a bit more; for when we take a longer view it is clear that life does more than replace itself: it achieves a progression in complexity, in awareness, in knowing. But we do not achieve this with only what we know. Each generation in creating its successor uses and transmits as best it can what it knows, the accumulated store of a thousand generations, but uses much more, uses meta-conscious patterns which cannot even in principle be encompassed in awareness. For had we to replace ourselves with but what we know and can specify, we could not make a single human being, would leave the earth to a progeny of sophisticated robots which, as they in turn reproduced themselves, would rapidly become less sophisticated, and soon vanish utterly.

No one has seen this more clearly than F. A. Hayek. "We always know," he writes, "not only more than we can deliberately state but also more than we can be aware of or deliberately test; and . . . much that we successfully do depends on presuppositions which are outside the range of what we can either state or reflect upon." [1] This vision must alter our concept of man.

Christianity created an image of man as innately bad. For many hundreds of years, to understand man was to recognize his fallen state, to accept original sin, to feel guilt, and under priestly supervision to do penance, trying to be good, failing, confessing, trying again with contrite heart, failing always, until at last, weary and broken, we fall into the arms of our Father who, moved by Christ's sacrifice, forgives us.

The Enlightenment destroyed this view. Man is innately good and reasonable, becomes bad only through the influence of bad institutions. Our task is to reshape these shaping institutions. This vision of man generated a wave of hope and optimism greater perhaps than the world had ever known. Original sin was replaced by original goodness and with it man began to design a good world by the use of reason. Hébert and Chaumette instituted the worship of reason as a new religion. God was banished and his institutions abolished. A Feast of Reason was celebrated in Notre Dame, a pretty actress taking the role of the Goddess of Reason. But the Revolution brought, not paradise, but Terror—Robespierre suspected treachery, Chaumette to save himself renounced Hébert, Robespierre beheaded them both, was then himself beheaded—and from the Terror came Napoleon, and all over Europe men were dying on battlefields.

But the ideology of revolution was not spent, was just beginning. In 1848 there was another wave, another attempt to build a good society by the blueprints of reason.[2] Marx mocked the new regime with the slogan of 1789: "Liberty, Equality, Fraternity . . . what this republic really means is Infantry, Cavalry, Artillery. . . ."[3] but did not mock as a cynic, was still dreaming Rousseau's dream, still believing it possible to build the good society by conscious design, still confident he knew the way. And eventually he had his chance: the blueprints were let out and

Russia returned the lowest bid; and though the architect didn't live to see it, master-builder Lenin followed the plan. The world has watched now for fifty years but has seen no good society; and most of us, were we forced to choose, would sooner take our chances in the police state of the Czars than in the police state of the commissars.

In this century, in a mood of deepening disillusionment, we have come to feel that man has no nature, good or bad, but is infinitely plastic. We are what we do, and may do as we choose. We cannot look within for guidance, cannot be true to ourselves because our selves have no fixed design but are shaped by what we do; and there is nothing anywhere, neither God up there nor identity within, that can with authority tell us what to do. Our freedom is more radical and more dangerous than ever before.

This is the age of 1984. Everything is permitted. We may become devils or gods. The heroes of one war are the cowards of the next, and the nation which is friend to its neighbor in one generation may come in the next as conqueror. We are what we do, and those who hold power, who control the ever more sophisticated and effective media, can persuade the rest of us to do whatever they wish us to do, even perhaps to believe it is we who are so wishing. Man has no nature, writes Ortega y Gasset, only history.

Now this vision, too, is fading. Our time of arrogance is coming to an end. We cannot go back, cannot believe again in a fixed human nature, good or bad, but are learning to accept a fundamental ignorance. Not an ignorance to be conquered by more knowing, but one which will recede forever before our ever longer cognitive reach, recede and grow larger, never even in principle to be eliminated.[4] It is true we are what we do, and true we can do as we

112

choose, but always we do and choose more than we know, achieve more than we intend. Luther nails his demands on the door at Wittenberg with a clear sense of choice, of taking a stand; and the freedom is no illusion, is real—for he might have chosen otherwise, and in no sense can his act be necessarily derived from any antecedent state—yet in so choosing he makes reference to more than he can know, and achieves more than he wills. Our lives rest on foundations unknown and unknowable. Our ignorance is structural and necessary.[5]

Those persons most intoxicated by the growth of knowledge, writes Hayek, are those most likely to become the enemies of freedom. For they conceive each gain in knowing as diminishing ignorance in corresponding degree, and imagine that because our gains in knowing have been so enormous in recent decades our ignorance may now be assumed to have shrunk to insignificant size. It must be time then to use our knowledge in the deliberate reorganization of society according to rational plan. Some resistance, they admit, may still be encountered from the uninformed and the reactionary; so an increase in coercion may for a time be necessary, perhaps for a generation or two, but is justified by the greater freedom and equality eventually to be realized.

But ignorance bears no such reciprocal relation to knowledge. The relation is direct, ignorance growing in the same measure as knowledge.[6]

Prior to the Modern Age we always found something beyond our experience by which to measure life, some criterion of value which we could not judge which judged us. God told us what to do, at times wrote it out on tablets of stone. The commandments are inconsistent, gods war among themselves, change their minds, commit egregious follies, yet remain gods, beyond our judgment. We may disobey their law but may not repeal it, may make laws of our own but only within the framework of divine ordinance. An unjust law violates God's will. Crime remains an infraction, cannot be made just by legislation.

In the Modern Age God is dismissed, the transcendent criterion rejected. Man will know the world by the un-aided effort of reason; discovered knowledge will no longer be subject to veto by revealed knowledge.[7] So man *becomes* God, stands intoxicated with reason at the summit of the universe. In delirious celebration Kepler looks back over the path of discovery which led him to the laws of planetary motion: "Having perceived the first glimmer of dawn eighteen months ago, the light of day three months ago, but only a few days ago the plain sun of a most wonderful vision—nothing shall now hold me back. Yes, I give myself up to holy raving. I mockingly defy all mortals with this open confession: I have robbed the golden vessels of the Egyptians to make out of them a tabernacle for my God, far from the frontiers of Egypt. If you forgive me, I will rejoice. If you are angry, I shall bear it. Behold, I have cast the dice, I am writing a book either for my contemporaries, or for posterity. It is all the same to me. It may wait a hundred years for a reader, since God has also waited six thousand years for a witness. . . ."[8]

This changed vision of man begins in the understanding of the material world but does not remain there, spreads to include man himself, his ways of living together. If we no longer need God's help in understanding the universe, why should we need it in understanding ourselves? Should we not in the light of pure reason know good and evil? And should we not then act on this knowledge to reshape life on earth?

So begins the age of reason and of revolution. Having eaten of the forbidden fruit, we proceed toward the creation of paradise on earth, following blueprints of our own design. War follows war, dictatorship follows revolution, the state grows ever stronger, and the state is the source of legitimate violence. Paradise has become a prison awash with blood.

The nineteenth century begins to hear a minor theme under the major chords of reason. Nihilism appears in Europe as a cancer of the spirit, metastasizes across the world. Everything is permitted, nothing withheld, nothing forbidden. We may do as we will, by fiat may establish right and wrong. There is no such thing then as an unjust law; for justice is defined by law, law is enacted by legislatures, legislatures are controlled by political power. Political power, therefore, determines right and wrong.[9]

In this position we know we have gone too far. We can't prove it, but we know in our hearts that some things are wrong in a way that no legislation could ever make right. We know, even without God, that "unjust law" is not a contradiction, not an absurdity, but a terrifying reality. We know, even if the legalized murder of Jews in Nazi Germany had, by virtue of the triumph of German armies and the spread of German influence, been supported by the enactment of similar laws and the instigation of similar procedures in all countries of the world, that all these laws would still be unjust, that no consensus of lawmakers could ever make them right.

In this conviction, to what authority do we appeal? It

transcends what we know and understand, yet we do not refer it back to God but retain it within ourselves.

We are more than we can know, so cannot be guided by rules that conform only to that part of ourselves which we can understand and communicate. We are what we do, but we do more than we intend. We do as we choose, but choose more than we prevision. Choice and action, therefore, entail consequences beyond those which reason can foresee. As rules of the game cannot be part of the play, so rules of life must lie beyond our living. The knowledge of good and evil is something we must seek to find, not aspire to determine.

"Nothing remains," Camus claims, "which can help us to answer the questions of our time. Absurdism, like methodical doubt, has wiped the slate clean." [10] But this, we would say, is precisely what has *not* happened. The slate can never be wiped clean, not by skepticism nor absurdity nor anything else, can be cleared only of what we control by knowing and know by controlling. And when we have cleared it of this there yet remains the invisible writing.

". . . No society is free," according to Berlin, "unless it is governed by at any rate two interrelated principles: first, that no power, but only rights, can be regarded as absolute, so that all men, whatever power governs them, have an absolute right to refuse to behave inhumanly; and, second, that there are frontiers, not artificially drawn, within which men should be inviolable, these frontiers being defined in terms of rules so long and widely accepted that their observance has entered into the very conception of what it is to be a normal human being, and, therefore, also of what it is to act inhumanly or insanely; rules of which it would be absurd to say, for example, that they could be abrogated by some formal procedure on the part of some court or sovereign body. When I speak of a man as being normal, a part of what I mean is that he could not break these rules easily, without a qualm of revulsion. It is such rules as these that are broken when a man is declared guilty without trial, or punished under a retroactive law; when children are ordered to denounce their parents, friends to betray one another, soldiers to use methods of barbarism; when men are tortured or murdered, or minorities are massacred because they irritate a majority or a tyrant. Such acts, even if they are made legal by the sovereign, cause horror even in these days, and this springs from the recognition of the moral validity—irrespective of the laws—of some absolute barriers to the imposition of one man's will on another." [11]

The liberalism of David Hume, Adam Smith, and Lord Acton holds that individual freedom under law permits the spontaneous generation of a social order, and that the order so arrived at is preferable to any that might be achieved by design. Such an order is without purpose, does not insure that any value or activity, however admirable, shall prevail or even exist. Under such an order it might come to pass that every home has color television but no books, that football teams abound but symphony orchestras disappear. Such matters, in the liberal view, are best left to the unforeseeable pattern which results from the free pursuit of individual destinies. Socialist theory demands that the effort of a collectivity be knowingly directed toward ends believed to be good; liberal theory holds that such endeavors, however noble in aim, lead to tyranny. "It is due to the fact that we do not enforce a unitary scale of concrete ends," writes F. A. Hayek, "nor attempt to secure that some particular view about what is more and what is less important governs the whole of society, that the members of such a free society have as good a chance successfully to use their individual knowledge for the achievement of their individual purposes as they in fact have." [12] The purposes which are important to liberal theory, therefore, are individual purposes. The social order should have none; but as this is not in practice possible, as few as may be.

A spontaneous order does not come about in all circumstances, but only if individuals obey rules of just conduct which protect a private domain of freedom. "Liberalism is therefore inseparable," says Hayek, "from the institution of private property which is the name we usually give to the material part of this protected individual domain." [13] As not all individuals will voluntarily obey rules, some coercion is always necessary. Liberalism accepts this, but would "restrict the *coercive* powers of government to the enforcement of such rules of just conduct." [14]

Arguing along the same lines, Karl Popper writes, "The state is a necessary evil, its powers are not to be multiplied beyond what is necessary." The state is necessary because, without it, even if all men were of good will "there would still be weaker and stronger men, and the weaker ones would have *no legal right* to be tolerated by the stronger ones, but would owe them gratitude for their being so kind as to tolerate them. Those (whether strong or weak) who think this an unsatisfactory state of affairs, and who think every person should have a *right* to live, and that every person should have a *legal claim* to be protected against the power of the strong, will agree that we need a state that protects the rights of all." [15]

Such protection is not a part of the spontaneous order, but is a condition for the formation of that order. It is, indeed, one of the *purposes* of the collective which, ideally, should be without purpose. Other purposes accrue. "Liberalism recognizes," Hayek explains, "that there are certain other services which for various reasons the spontaneous forces of the market may not produce or may not produce adequately, and that for this reason it is desirable to put at the disposal of the government a clearly circumscribed body of resources with which it can render such services to the citizens in general. This requires a sharp distinction between the coercive powers of government, in which its actions are strictly limited to the enforcement of rules of just conduct and in the exercise of which all discretion is excluded, and the provision of services by government, for which it can use only the resources put at its disposal for this purpose, has no coercive power or monopoly, but in the use of which resources it enjoys wide discretion." [16]

The distinction which Hayek here draws so sharply does not remain sharp. Are corporations and labor unions quasi-individuals subject only to rules governing individuals? Or should we, observing the enormous power they achieve, at times becoming principalities within the state, regard them as special cases, and impose upon the state the additional purpose of holding them under surveillance and subjecting them to different rules? With increasing industrialization social life becomes more complex, and the responsibilities and purposes of the state proliferate—none more rapidly nor more ominously than national defense. For the protection of the collective cannot be left to the spontaneous order, requires a planned policy, becomes the overriding purpose of the state. To achieve it, coercion is extended far beyond the enforcing of rules of just conduct, men are compelled to bear arms, huge military establishments are construed to be necessary, paramilitary and espionage forces are created, an industrial readiness for all-out weapons production is maintained. Such readiness for war may consume half the resources of the collective, may come in time to determine domestic policy as well as foreign policy.

Purposes multiply endlessly, and with them power; governments which profess liberal principles become steadily more socialistic. Western democracies have been driven toward socialism, writes Hayek, by "the growing recognition that the application of uniform or equal rules to the conduct of individuals who were in fact very different in many respects, inevitably produced very different results for the different individuals; and that in order to bring about by government action a reduction in these unintended but inevitable differences in the material position of different people, it would be necessary to treat them not according to the same but according to different rules. This gave rise to a new and altogether different conception of justice, namely that usually described as 'social' or 'distributive' justice, a conception of justice which did not confine itself to rules of conduct for the individual but aimed at particular results for particular people, and which therefore could be achieved only in a purpose-governed organization but not in a purpose-independent spontaneous order." [17]

So it comes about that a national state conceived to be without purpose, to function only in the maintenance of a rule of law which allows the infinite interactions of individual purposes to create a spontaneous order, becomes so powerful, so loaded with duties and purposes, always extending its range of coercion, that no order within it can be deemed the spontaneous creation of freely interacting individual destinies. The free economy was more dream than fact even when first described by Hume and Smith; now, after the technological and organizational changes of the last three hundred years, it is but the memory of a dream.

We know more than we can say, and if by leap of spirit we come to be able to say that which, until then, we had been unable to know, at that moment we will have created something more beyond even that which we then can say. We are governed by rules that lie beyond the rules we make, and the rules we make must accord with those rules which go before us. They are the product of our experience but not of our design. We cannot seize them in the grasp of knowing, can but sense them as a limit to be honored, which only pride might tempt us to violate.

We must not demand to understand all. For if we recognize only what reason can grasp we are led to infinite regress: law is justified by principle, principle by value, value by assumption and so on until we arrive at a paralysis from which we can escape only by declaring that law needs no justification, that its authority derives from its enactment —that is, from political power. But the moment we take this stand we find that we have created a world in which there cannot in principle be an unjust law, even if law call for the murder of the innocent. That way leads to Terror.

X

Progress

W E have every reason to believe," wrote Edward Westermarck in 1908, concluding his panoramic survey of morality, "that the altruistic sentiment will continue to expand, and that those moral commandments which are based on it will undergo a corresponding expansion, that the influence of reflection upon moral judgments will steadily increase." [1]

The years since then have not been good to the idea of moral progress.[2] The image of progress has fallen into two pieces which drift ever further apart. Hardly anyone now believes it possible to bring them together. In knowledge of the material world, the ability to constrain its energies to our purposes, there is a clear difference between ourselves and the people of any past age; in morality, a remarkable sameness. In 416 B.C., according to Thucydides, the Athenians took Melos, put to death all the grown men, "sold the women and children for slaves, and subsequently sent out five hundred colonists and inhabited the place themselves." [3] In 1901 Kitchener systematically denuded the farmlands of the Boers, herded the women and children into concentration camps where twenty thousand died of starvation, disease, neglect, and despair.[4]

In the absence of moral progress technological progress becomes a questionable good. For technological progress is always an increase in power, and if we who gain power gain nothing in goodness we become more dangerous. It has, indeed, become vulgar to be proud of such progress, and those persons concerned with goodness fall silent about the triumphs of science. Young people turn away from televised moon-landings, forget the electric razor, let their hair grow long, wander the highways and the wilderness, away from supermarkets, away even from flush toilets, in search of something sacred. If scientific progress doesn't lead to greater loving, they seem to say, what good is it?

This attitude is new to our time; for throughout the Modern Age the vision of social betterment has rested on the growth of scientific knowledge. Even after World War I we still believed the social sciences would "catch up." The young of those days cheered Lindbergh on his flight, and whether they followed John Dewey or Lenin they were as one in the belief in science. We now remember Dewey as a well-meaning uncle from our childhood, a guide to a more innocent world; and Lenin we remember with dismay. The blueprints of paradise justified the purging of millions; and the victory of democracy flowered in fascism and death camps. The bombs have grown bigger, the planes faster; and the grandchildren of those of us who cheered the *Spirit of St. Louis* now sneer at the supersonic transport. Those who still commit themselves to science do not concern themselves with morality: it has proven refractive to scientific method, they seem to say, it is swayed by opinion, is relative to time and place and custom, so can have nothing to do with the verifiable propositions of science, and is disparaged by being ignored.

We must grant the case is made: within recorded history we see no progress in morals. But we can take a longer view, can see far beyond man's years of record, of his struggles with God, can see back several hundred thousand years during which he kept no diary, left only stone implements, from which, however, we make out a line of development leading away from his animal forebears toward greater awareness, greater knowing. And we can see beyond that to an animal primate beginning to walk upright, more interested in looking than in sniffing. And further, when there were no primates, and beyond that; and though our knowledge stretches thin it does reach a time when there was no life at all on this cinder flying about the sun.

We see a time, therefore, when morality did not exist. It comes into existence with man, so cannot be more than a million years old. Man looks at the world as did his primate ancestors, but, unlike them, looks also at himself looking, knows himself knowing, observes himself acting. When awareness expands to include consciousness itself, options are perceived and freedom is created. Then one can say, "I see this hungry stranger, and the club in his hands, I know how he can wield it and to what effect, and I see, also, that he is afraid. I am aware, further, of my own fear and anger, and also of compassion, for I know how it feels to be hungry in a strange land, and so I become aware of choice: I can kill him or feed him. At this moment both are possible. Which is better?" In such choice is born freedom and morality. They come together. Neither can exist alone.

As nothing in life is beyond change, morality cannot be a fixed attribute. It began somewhere in the course of our expanding awareness, as a consequence of that expansion.

We know that awareness has increased enormously during the last million years, measurably even within our own few thousand years of record. And freedom has increased likewise; the range of choice is far greater now than when our forebears chipped the first flint, greater than when Sargon welded together the first empire. To find in this long view a beginning of morality does not guarantee the growth of morality, but reminds us that it is an aspect of a form of life which had a known beginning and will likely have an end, and that within that span all its attributes, including the moral sense, are likely to evolve.

From the crooked timber of humanity, wrote Kant, no straight thing was ever made. And the course of moral progress, if not altogether an illusion, is the despair of seekers after the straight line, is to be discerned if at all only in curved lines and coalescences. Empathy emanates from each person, is often obliterated by hostility, but is never altogether absent; for no one is so mean-spirited as to be incapable of caring. Like ripples on the surface of a pond, empathy radiates from personal centers through an interpersonal field. A solitary hunter wandering an empty world would encounter nothing to reinforce his meager center of caring, would radiate diminishing concern like a failing flashlight in a jungle. But we are not alone, and waves of empathy encounter each other, coalesce; and presently caring achieves such intensity that several persons form a group. Families fuse into tribes, and tribes into nations. So grows the moral order.[5]

And so, likewise, grows evil. For this path of curved lines and coalescences on which we trace the course of moral progress is the same on which we may follow also the growth of murder and pillage. The solitary hunter will have murdered perhaps a single man; but when he has been welded by love into a tribe, his tribe will murder another tribe, and when many tribes have become a nation, that nation will destroy another nation.

We live with differing degrees of commitment and loyalty in an ascending hierarchy of associations, each a whole with some measure of independence, and each a component of some larger whole. Within hours we read the book of a French author, listen to music of a German performed by a Russian, eat Greek olives, wear Thai silk, and photograph our daughter with a Japanese camera. The various hierarchies—political, industrial, social, ideological, vocational—touch and diverge and interweave. All serve to extend awareness, to create widening realms of relatedness and empathy. Most crucial to our security is the political hierarchy, for it is here that power is held and wielded.

The furthermost limits of secure community depend upon empathy, upon how far afield we can take the part of the other, can rely upon ourselves for both goodness and morality. Empathy, in turn, depends upon awareness and understanding; for we cannot identify ourselves with life we know not of. Awareness does not insure empathy, but without it empathy is not possible. The more we know of others, of what they fear, what makes them happy, the more likely we are to feel with them and for them.

The strength of empathy is an inverse function of emotional distance: the deeper our relatedness to others the stronger our identifications with them. We most easily take the part of the other within the family. At the range of neighborhood we are not so inclined; a cry for help may go unheeded.[6] At the limit of nation empathy is even more tenuous, and beyond this limit becomes so thin that we call

129

people foreigners; when conflict comes, the slender strands of empathy dissolve in anger and we destroy them.

The willing subordination of individuals to the shared principles of a group proceeds upward in the hierarchy, upward in the sense of developmentally later, organizationally more complex, quantitatively comprehensive of greater number and greater variety. People learn to live together amicably as a tribe before they learn, as tribes, to live together amicably as a nation.

In our time there exists a relatively secure community within the several nations, while the nations together form but a precarious community. Like faults in the earth's crust, fracture points lie along the borders, along the rivers and mountains, the Berlin Walls and Maginot Lines which mark the outer limits to which we can rely upon ourselves to mean everybody when we say "we." We will send our emissaries and our empathy around the world, but when trouble comes we will withdraw to these boundaries from which we will look out on our erstwhile neighbor along the barrel of a gun. Waves of empathy reach round the world, make no great splash at the antipodes, yet reach, have reached so far since the first circumnavigation of the globe. During these four hundred years we have encountered many "foreigners" for whom we felt little empathy. We of the West, having always been better armed, have often enslaved and destroyed them.

Life moves toward greater awareness. Earthworm tunnels the earth, so knows it better than leaf mold, though not so well as bird. Living forms become ever more complex, structurally more differentiated, thereby more able to know the world, to know it both more truly and more widely. Leaf mold to earthworm to bird to fox to monkey to man—each step in this development brings greater vision. In man this process accelerates, enters a different realm. The slow evolution which over millions of years depended upon biological change now, in the course of but a few thousand, becomes a process which issues from changes in culture, proceeds at a rate which ever increases. The direction of change is toward greater knowing, wider and deeper awareness.[7] At the furthermost reach of awareness we always find strangers; but empathy follows sooner or later upon awareness, and strangers become persons like ourselves.

Conflict is ever present, always threatens empathy. Fighting can break out anywhere, even within a family. We are concerned here, not to condemn conflict, nor to hope for a heaven without it, but to ask where, when a breaking point is reached, the bonds of empathy will give way. In the Modern Age these bonds have been relatively stable up to and including the national level; civil wars have been rather the exception than the rule. But the ties which unite the several nations into one community have been weak, and the breaking point has been at national boundaries. In view of the weapons with which nations are now armed, this offers neither comfort nor security, but in the long view of man's past becomes one point on a curve the trajectory of which can bear the name of progress.

For once man roved the earth in predatory bands, and between such bands empathy was as tenuous as now it is between nations, and when it failed, as often it did, one band would destroy another. In Neolithic times man lived in villages, and in times of trouble one village would destroy another. With the beginning of civilization city made war on city. Then cities were forged into nations, nations into empires. Four thousand years ago Sargon united the Sumerians and the Akkadians in the first fragile model of that political entity which dominates the modern world. In Sargon's time the condition of agricultural and industrial arts, of communication and transport, made such political aggregates unstable; empires were constantly falling apart. In our time science and technology endow far larger political communities with great stability.

The secure community grows larger. The secure community is that association of people which is relatively free of the danger of breaking apart into warring factions which destroy each other. The path of moral progress is one of increasing awareness, creating an ever-widening field of empathy within which we take the part of the other, which leads in turn to an ever more inclusive hierarchy of communities, pushing ever outward the fault line, so that when conflict occurs the warring fragments are themselves ever larger. As we live on a sphere, such expansion of empathy may eventually bind the earth in a secure community.

Notes

Numbers in parentheses refer to Works Cited (pp. 157–159).

I
Nihilism

1. *Newsweek*, January 3, 1972, p. 20.
2. San Francisco *Chronicle*, April 28, 1971.
3. In 1521 Cortés laid siege to Tenochtitlán, capital of the Aztecs. In the course of a premature assault on the city sixty-two Spaniards were taken captive. The next day Alvarado, lieutenant to Cortés, heard the great drum in the temple of the war-god and beheld a long procession winding up the huge sides of the pyramid. "As the long file of priests and warriors reached the flat summit of the *teocalli*," writes Prescott, "the Spaniards saw the figures of several men stripped to their waists, some of whom, by the whiteness of their skins, they recognized as their own countrymen. They were the victims for sacrifice. Their heads were gaudily decorated with coronals of plumes, and they carried fans in their hands. They were urged along by blows, and compelled to take part in the dances in honor of the Aztec war-god. The unfortunate captives, then stripped of their sad finery, were stretched, one after another, on the great stone of sacrifice. On its convex surface, their breasts were heaved up conveniently for the diabolical purpose of the priestly executioner, who cut asunder the ribs by a strong blow with his sharp razor of *itzli*, and, thrusting his hand into the wound, tore away the heart, which, hot and reeking, was deposited in the golden censer before the idol. The body of the slaughtered victim was then hurled down the steep stairs of the pyramid . . . and the mutilated remains were gathered up by the savages beneath, who soon prepared with them a cannibal repast." Prescott (36), II, 251–252.
4. Words of Richard Hilary who was killed in combat in World War II, quoted by Camus (12), p. 248.
5. Dostoyevsky (15), p. 254.
6. Quoted by Camus (11), p. 65.
7. The most exalted love, Lou Andreas-Salome writes in her diary, "can become sensuous again, precisely because of its emotional intensifi-

cation of the ideal. It is an unpleasant fact, this revenge of the body. I do not like circular feelings that return from whence they came, for that is the point of false pathos, of lost honesty and truth of feeling. Is it this, perhaps, which alienates me from Nietzsche?" Quoted by Peters (32), p. 133.

8. A changing tide of civilization, writes Lecky, does not repudiate opinions that stand opposed; it simply renders them obsolete. "They perish by indifference, not by controversy. They are relegated to the dim twilight land that surrounds every living faith; the land, not of death, but of the shadow of death; the land of the unrealized and the inoperative." Lecky (24), I, xxi.

9. "It all seems to have been in vain," said Harry Truman, speaking of his presidential career. "Memories are short and appetites for power and glory are insatiable. Old tyrants depart. New ones take their places. Old differences are composed, new differences arise. Old allies become the foe. The recent enemy becomes the friend. It's all very baffling and trying." Commenting on these remarks, *The New Yorker* sounds the modern tone: "Since Heraclitus, mankind has been in possession of the truth that everything flows. Flux is the ground wherein men and states alike achieve their provisional victories, which are not meaningless because they become obsolete. The search for peace is a search not for a fixed object but for a temporary adjustment, a balance of aggressions; we do not agree with those who view a master of patchwork—like, say, Metternich—as somehow absurd because an eventual holocaust unravelled everything. In an interim of truce, thousands of babies can be born healthy and thousands of old people can die in their beds. There is nothing undignified or futile about buying time; it is the only item on the counter." *The New Yorker*, February 5, 1966.

10. Looking back over the panorama of witchcraft, the hundreds of thousands of women, mostly poor, ignorant, eccentric women, who were burned at the stakes of Christendom, Lecky asks how it could happen, how can we even conceive of it coming about that in so many different countries, over so many hundreds of years, before so many thousands of tribunals, secular as well as ecclesiastical, men of intelligence and good will should continue to have found absolute and incontrovertible evidence of evil-doing by witches. It is difficult to examine this subject, he writes, "without coming to the conclusion that the historical evidence establishing the reality of witchcraft is so vast and so varied that it is impossible to disbelieve it without what, on other subjects, we should deem the most extraordinary rashness. The defenders of the belief, who were often men of great and distinguished talent, maintained that there was no fact in all history more fully attested." Some cases, he suggests, "may be explained by monomania, others by imposture, others by chance coincidences, and others by optical delusions; but, when we consider the multitude of strange statements that were sworn and registered in legal documents, it is very difficult to

frame a general rationalistic explanation which will not involve an extreme improbability." We can understand only if, by imagination, we recreate a world in which "men believe that invisible beings, of superhuman power, restless activity, and intense malignity, are perpetually haunting the world, and directing all their energies to the temptation and the persecution of mankind; . . . that, in past ages, these spirits have actually governed the bodily functions of men, worked miracles, and foretold future events,—if all this is believed, not with the dull and languid assent of custom, but with an intensely realized, living, and operative assurance; if it presents itself to the mind and the imagination as a vivid truth, exercising that influence over the reason, and occupying that prominence in the thoughts of men, which its importance would demand," only then can we understand the measures our ancestors took to deal with witches. Lecky (24), I, 14–16.

Lecky also notes that every change of belief has been preceded by a change in intellectual condition, and that the success of any opinion depends "less upon the force of its arguments, or upon the ability of its advocates, than upon the predisposition of society to receive it." Such predisposition results from the intellectual type which characterizes the age. "A change of speculative opinions," he writes, "does not imply an increase of the data upon which those opinions rest, but a change of the habits of thought and mind which they reflect. Definite arguments are the symptoms and pretext, but seldom the causes, of the change . . . [they] derive their force and efficacy from their conformity with the mental habits of those to whom they are addressed." The number of persons who "have a rational basis for their belief is probably infinitesimal; for illegitimate influences not only determine the convictions of those who do not examine, but usually give a dominating bias to the reasoning of those who do. . . . All that we can rightly infer is that the process of reasoning is much more difficult than is commonly supposed; and that to those who would investigate the causes of existing opinions, the study of predispositions is much more important than the study of arguments." Lecky (24), I, vi, vii, xv.

"Whether arguments command assent or not," writes Carl Becker, "depends less upon the logic that conveys them than upon the climate of opinion in which they are sustained." What renders the work of Dante or Thomas Aquinas meaningless to us "is not bad logic or want of intelligence, but the medieval climate of opinion—those instinctively held preconceptions in the broad sense, that *Weltanschauung* or world pattern—which imposed upon Dante and St. Thomas a peculiar use of the intelligence and a special type of logic." We cannot meet their arguments on their own ground, "can neither assent to them nor refute them. It does not even occur to us to make the effort, since we instinctively feel that in the climate of opinion which sustains such arguments we could only gasp for breath." Their conclusions seem to us neither true nor false, but irrelevant, because the "world pattern into which they are so dextrously woven is no longer capable of eliciting from us either an emotional or an esthetic response." Becker (3), pp. 5, 11–12.

11. Becker (3), p. 15.

II

Antitheses of Morality

1. Berlin (4), p. lv.

2. Quoted by Carr (13), p. 395.

3. "Alexander Herzen," May 1956, in *Encounters: An Anthology from the First Ten Years of* Encounter *Magazine* (New York: Basic Books, 1963), p. 334.

4. Max Weber, "Politics as a Vocation," in Gerth and Mills (17), pp. 120–127. Italics in the original.

5. Cf. Hayek (19), p. 230.

6. "The world that we encounter in ordinary experience," Berlin observes, "is one in which we are faced with choices between ends equally ultimate, and claims equally absolute, the realization of some of which must inevitably involve the sacrifice of others. Indeed, it is because this is their situation that men place such immense value upon the freedom to choose; for if they had assurance that in some perfect state, realizable by men on earth, no ends pursued by them would ever be in conflict, the necessity and agony of choice would disappear, and with it the central importance of the freedom to choose. Any method of bringing this final state nearer would then seem fully justified, no matter how much freedom were sacrificed to forward its advance . . . [But] if, as I believe, the ends of men are many, and not all of them are in principle compatible with each other, then the possibility of conflict—and of tragedy—can never wholly be eliminated from human life, either personal or social. The necessity of choosing between absolute claims is then an inescapable characteristic of the human condition. This gives its value to freedom as Acton had conceived of it—as an end in itself, and not as a temporary need, arising out of our confused notions and irrational and disordered lives, a predicament which a panacea could one day put right." Berlin (4), pp. 168–169.

III

Goodness and Morality

1. "It is the nature of narration," writes Lionel Trilling, "to explain; it cannot help telling how things are and even why they are that way.

How did death come into the world and all that woe? Well, I will tell you—'In the beginning . . .' But a beginning implies an end, with something in the middle to connect them. The beginning is not merely the first of a series of events; it is the event that originates those that follow. And the end is not merely the ultimate event, the cessation of happening; it is a significance or at least the promise, dark or bright, of a significance. The tale is not told by an idiot but by a rational consciousness which perceives in things the processes that are their reason and which derives from this perception a principle of conduct, a way of living among things." Trilling (42), pp. 135–136.

2. Ibid., p. 138.

3. Quoted, ibid., p. 138.

4. In our times, writes J. H. Plumb, the past is dying. "The new methods, new processes, new forms of living of scientific and industrial society have no sanction in the past and no roots in it. The past becomes, therefore, a matter of curiosity, of nostalgia, of sentimentality." Plumb (33), pp. 14, 15. It informs us of no direction, assures us of no destiny. The telling of tales becomes pointless. As Trilling observes, "A chief part of the inauthenticity of narration would seem to be its assumption that life is susceptible of comprehension and thus of management." Trilling (42), p. 135.

5. "In this state of things," he continues, "it was beneficently ordered by Providence that the land should be delivered over to another race, who would rescue it from the brutish superstitions that daily extended wider and wider, with the extent of empire. The debasing institutions of the Aztecs furnish the best apology for their conquest. It is true, the conquerors brought along with them the Inquisition. But they also brought Christianity, whose benign radiance would still survive, when the fierce flames of fanaticism should be extinguished; dispelling those dark forms of horror which had so long brooded over the fair regions of Anahuac." Prescott (36), I, 79–80.

6. Quoted by E. H. Carr, *The Romantic Exiles*, p. 63 (Boston: Beacon Press, 1961. First published in 1933 by Victor Gollancz, Ltd., London).

7. "Every man," Kirk continues, "must decide for himself according to his own estimate of conditions and consequences; and no one can decide for him or impugn the decision to which he comes. Perhaps this is the end of the matter after all." *Conscience and Its Problems* (London: Longmans, Green and Co., Ltd., 1927), p. 331, quoted by Fletcher (16), p. 36.

8. Quoted by Schlesinger (39), p. 76.

9. Ibid., p. 77.

10. Niebuhr (31), quoted by Schlesinger (39), p. 72.

11. Schlesinger (39), p. 73.

12. "Love is an imperious law unto itself. It will not share its power. It will not share its authority with any other laws, either natural or su-

pernatural. Love is even capable of desecrating the Holy of Holies, the very tabernacle of the altar, if human hunger cries for help." Fletcher (16), pp. 60, 85, 87.

13. "One belief, more than any other," writes Isaiah Berlin, "is responsible for the slaughter of individuals on the altars of the great historical ideals—justice or progress or the happiness of future generations, or the sacred mission or emancipation of a nation or race or class, or even liberty itself, which demands the sacrifice of individuals for the freedom of society. This is the belief that somewhere, in the past or in the future, in divine revelation or in the mind of an individual thinker, in the pronouncements of history or science, or in the simple heart of an uncorrupted good man, there is a final solution. This ancient faith rests on the conviction that all the positive values in which men have believed must, in the end, be compatible, and perhaps even entail one another. . . . [But it] is a commonplace that neither political equality nor efficient organization nor social justice is compatible with more than a modicum of individual liberty, and certainly not with unrestricted *laissez-faire;* that justice and generosity, public and private loyalties, the demands of genius and the claims of society, can conflict violently with each other." Berlin (4), p. 167.

14. "The growth from the tribal organization," he continues, "all of whose members served common purposes, to the spontaneous order of the Open Society in which people are allowed to pursue their own purposes in peace, may thus be said to have commenced when for the first time a savage placed some goods at the boundary of his tribe in the hope that some member of another tribe would find them and leave in turn behind some other goods to secure the repetition of the offer. From the first establishment of such a practice which served reciprocal but not common purposes, a process has been going on for milennia which, by making rules of conduct independent of the particular purposes of those concerned, made it possible to extend these rules to ever wider circles of undetermined persons and eventually might make possible a universal peaceful order of the world." Hayek (19), pp. 166–168.

15. Cf. Camus (11).

IV

Slavery and Rebellion

1. "When the throne of God is overturned, the rebel realizes that it is now his own responsibility to create the justice, order, and unity that he sought in vain within his own condition, and in this way to justify the fall of God. Then begins the desperate effort to create, at the price of crime and murder if necessary, the dominion of man. . . ." Camus (11), p. 25. "A revolutionary action," he writes in another context,

Notes

"which wishes to be coherent in terms of its origins should be embodied in an active consent to the relative. It would express fidelity to the human condition. Uncompromising as to its means, it would accept an approximation as far as its ends are concerned and, so that the approximation should become more and more accurately defined, it would allow absolute freedom of speech. Thus it would preserve the common existence that justifies its insurrection. In particular, it would preserve as an absolute law the permanent possibility of self expression. This defines a particular line of conduct in regard to justice and freedom. There is no justice in society without natural or civil rights as its basis. There are no rights without expression of those rights. If the rights are expressed without hesitation it is more than probable that, sooner or later, the justice they postulate will come to the world. To conquer existence, we must start from the small amount of existence we find in ourselves and not deny it from the very beginning. To silence the law until justice is established is to silence it forever since it will have no more occasion to speak if justice reigns forever. . . . Absolute non-violence is the negative basis of slavery and its acts of violence; systematic violence positively destroys the living community and the existence we receive from it. To be fruitful, these two ideas must establish final limits." Camus (11), pp. 290–291.

2. Mill (28), p. 73.

3. "One picture, only one more," says Ivan Karamazov, "because it's so curious, so characteristic. . . . There was in those days a general of aristocratic connections, the owner of great estates, one of those men —somewhat exceptional, I believe, even then—who, retiring from the service into a life of leisure, are convinced that they've earned absolute power over the lives of their subjects. There were such men then. So our general, settled on his property of two thousand souls, lives in pomp, and domineers over his poor neighbours as though they were dependents and buffoons. He has kennels of hundreds of hounds and nearly a hundred dog-boys—all mounted, and in uniform. One day a serf boy, a little child of eight, threw a stone in play and hurt the paw of the general's favourite hound. 'Why is my favourite dog lame?' He is told that the boy threw a stone that hurt the dog's paw. 'So you did it.' The general looked the child up and down. 'Take him.' He was taken —taken from his mother and kept shut up all night. Early that morning the general comes out on horseback, with the hounds, his dependents, dog-boys, and huntsmen, all mounted around him in full hunting parade. The servants are summoned for their edification, and in front of them all stands the mother of the child. The child is brought from the lock-up. It's a gloomy cold, foggy autumn day, a capital day for hunting. The general orders the child to be undressed; the child is stripped naked. He shivers, numb with terror, not daring to cry. . . . 'Make him run,' commands the general. 'Run! run!' shout the dog-boys. The boy runs. . . . 'At him!' yells the general, and he sets the whole pack of

hounds on the child. The hounds catch him, and tear him to pieces before his mother's eyes! . . ." Dostoyevsky (15), pp. 251–252.

4. Every act of rebellion, writes Camus, invokes a value. "Though it springs from everything that is most strictly individualistic in man, it questions the very idea of the individual. If the individual, in fact, accepts death and happens to die as a consequence of his act of rebellion, he demonstrates by doing so that he is willing to sacrifice himself for the sake of a common good which he considers more important than his own destiny. If he prefers the risk of death to the negation of the rights that he defends, it is because he considers these rights more important than himself. Therefore he is acting in the name of certain values which are still indeterminate but which he feels are common to himself and to all men. . . . The affirmation implicit in every act of rebellion is extended to something that transcends the individual in so far as it withdraws him from his supposed solitude and provides him with a reason to act. . . . It is for the sake of everyone in the world that the slave asserts himself when he comes to the conclusion that a command has infringed on something in him which does not belong to him alone, but which is common ground where all men—even the man who insults and oppresses him—have a natural community. . . . Therefore the individual is not, in himself alone, the embodiment of the values he wishes to defend. It needs all humanity, at least, to comprise them." Rebellion, therefore, is profoundly positive. It "enlists the individual in the defense of a dignity common to all men. . . . Man's solidarity is founded upon rebellion, and rebellion, in its turn, can find its justification only in this solidarity. We have, then, the right to say that any rebellion which claims the right to deny or destroy this solidarity loses simultaneously its right to be called rebellion and becomes in reality an acquiescence in murder. . . . If men cannot refer to a common value, recognized by all as existing in each one, then man is incomprehensible to man. The rebel demands that this value should be clearly recognized in himself because he knows or suspects that, without this principle, crime and disorder would reign throughout the world." An act of rebellion, therefore, is a demand for clarity and unity, expresses an aspiration to order. Camus (11), pp. 15–23.

5. "The most extreme form of freedom, the freedom to kill, is not compatible with the sense of rebellion," Camus observes. ". . . Rebellion puts total freedom up for trial . . . attacks the unlimited power that authorizes a superior to violate the forbidden frontier. Far from demanding general independence, the rebel wants it to be recognized that freedom has its limits everywhere that a human being is to be found—the limit being precisely that human being's power to rebel. The rebel . . . does not demand the right to destroy the existence and freedom of others. He humiliates no one. The freedom he claims, he claims for all; the freedom he refuses, he forbids everyone to enjoy. He is not only the slave against the master, but also man against the world of master and

slave. Therefore, thanks to rebellion, there is something more in history than the relation between mastery and servitude. Unlimited power is not the only law. It is in the name of another value that the rebel affirms the impossibility of total freedom while he claims for himself the relative freedom necessary to recognize this impossibility. Every human freedom, at its very roots, is therefore relative. Absolute freedom, which is the freedom to kill, is the only one which does not claim, at the same time as itself, the things that limit and obliterate it. Thus it cuts itself off from its roots and—abstract and malevolent shade—wanders haphazardly until such time as it imagines that it has found substance in some ideology." Camus (11), pp. 284–285.

V

Force and Authority

1. Popper (35), pp. 453–454. Italics in original.

2. Ibid., p. 461. Italics in original.

3. "Hume may be called a precursor to Darwin in the sphere of ethics. In effect, he proclaimed a doctrine of the survival of the fittest among human conventions—fittest . . . in terms of maximum social utility." Bay (2), p. 33. Rules of morality are the product of cultural evolution.

Our social institutions developed in the particular way they did, Hayek points out, because "the coordination of the actions of the parts they secured proved more effective than the alternative institutions with which they had competed and which they had displaced. The theory of evolution of traditions and habits which made the formation of spontaneous orders possible stands therefore in a close relation to the theory of evolution of the particular kinds of spontaneous orders which we call organisms." Hayek (19), p. 101. "What are called structures," writes L. von Bertalanffy, "are slow processes of long duration, functions are quick processes of short duration. If we say that a function such as a contraction of a muscle is performed by a structure, it means that a quick and short process-wave is superimposed on a long-lasting and slowly running wave." Quoted by Hayek (19), p. 101.

4. "Not only," he continues, "does all made law *aim* at justice and *not create* justice, not only has no made law ever succeeded in replacing all the already recognized rules of justice which it presupposes or even succeeded in dispensing with explicit references to such inarticulated conceptions of justice; but the whole process of development, change and interpretation of law would become wholly unintelligible if we closed our eyes to the existence of a framework of such unarticulated rules from which the articulated law receives its meaning." Hayek (19), p. 102.

Yet positivism, he points out, "still clings to the essentially anthropomorphic view which regards all rules of justice as the product of deliberate invention or design. . . . The most serious effect of the dominance of that view has been that it leads necessarily to the destruction of all belief in a justice which can be found and not merely decreed by the will of a legislator. If law is wholly the product of deliberate design, whatever the designer decrees to be law is just by definition and unjust law becomes a contradiction in terms. The will of the duly authorized legislator is then wholly unfettered and guided solely by his concrete interests." Such legal positivism is the application to legal theory of the rationalist constructivism of Descartes, and its argument proves only that such an approach cannot arrive at any criterion for justice. If we realize, however, that "law is never wholly the product of design but is judged and tested within a framework of rules of justice nobody has invented and which guided people's thinking and actions even before those rules were ever expressed in words, we obtain, though not a positive, yet still a negative criterion of justice which enables us, by progressively eliminating all rules which are incompatible with the rest of the system, gradually to approach (though perhaps never to reach) absolute justice." Hayek (19), pp. 101–103.

5. The artistic placing and management of news, "quite inevitable at the electric speed that involves the entire society in the decision-making process, shocks the old pressmen because it abdicates any definite point of view. As the speed of information increases, the tendency is for politics to move away from representation and delegation of constituents toward immediate involvement of the entire community in the central acts of decision." High-speed information, McLuhan says, makes traditional democracy obsolete. It "can only be made to function by a series of subterfuges and makeshifts. These strike some observers as base betrayals of the original aims and purposes of the established forms." McLuhan (26), pp. 203–204.

6. I. F. Stone informs us that the first indication that the U.S. Information Agency was secretly subsidizing books is found in the House Appropriations Committee hearings released in December 1965. Reed Harris of U.S.I.A. is asked to explain a $195,000 item for "Book Development." He said this was a program "under which we can have books written to our own specifications, books that would not otherwise be put out, especially those books that have strong anti-Communist content, and follow other themes that are particularly useful for our purposes. Under the book development program we control the thing from the very idea down to the final edited manuscript." When the hearings were published, the names of the books and their authors were blacked out "because," as Harris explained, "our interest in certain of these books should not become a matter of general public information." The books were published by American publishers and sold within the United States. Nothing about them would lead a reader to suspect they

were financed and cleared by the government. Upon being asked why the American people should not know of the government sponsorship, Mr. Leonard H. Marks, Director of the U.S. Information Agency, said: "It minimizes their value. . . . If we say this is our book, then the author is a government employee, in effect. It changes the whole status of the author. . . ." The overseas distribution, Mr. Marks admitted, was propaganda; but he would not admit that the sale of these books in the United States was propaganda. When it was pointed out that he was drawing an awfully fine line here, he delivered himself as follows: "Propaganda has to be defined. I would like to go into this very briefly. Propaganda has the overtones of Hitler Germany where there is lying, where there is a misrepresentation. I do not believe in that. I have said time and again that all we have to do is tell the truth." (House Approp. 1965 Hearings, pp. 620–622. Reported in *I. F. Stone's Weekly*, October 17, 1966.)

7. "That cascade of peremptory affirmatives," writes Camus, "that sententious style, portrays him better than the most faithful painting. His sentences drone on; his definitions follow one another with the coldness and precision of commandments. 'Principles should be moderate, laws implacable, principles without redress.' It is the style of the guillotine. . . . The man who with such nobility held that it was infamous to lay down one's arms while there remained, somewhere in the world, one master and one slave, is the same man who had to agree to suspend the Constitution of 1793 and to adopt arbitrary rule."

In the end he was himself engulfed by the Terror to which his principles led him. "The guillotine is going to fall again," Camus continues, "on that head as cold and beautiful as morality itself. From the moment that the Assembly condemns him until the moment when he stretches his neck to the knife, Saint-Just keeps silent. This long silence is more important than his death. He complained that silence reigned around thrones and that is why he wanted to speak so much and so well. But in the end, contemptuous of the tyranny and the enigma of a people who do not conform to pure reason, he resorts to silence himself. His principles do not allow him to accept things as they are; and, things not being what they should be, his principles are therefore fixed, silent, and alone. To abandon oneself to principles is really to die—and to die for an impossible love which is the contrary of love." Camus (11), pp. 125, 127, 129–130.

VI

We and They

1. Cf. Niebuhr (31), pp. 95ff. Adolph Harnack, eminent German theologian, represents his country's position at the beginning of World War

I as follows: "England cuts the dyke which has preserved western Europe and its civilization from the encroaching desert of Russia and Pan-Slavism. We must hold out for we must defend the work of fifteen hundred years for Europe and for England itself." Quoted by Niebuhr (31), pp. 97–98. (This curious image seems to betray an awareness of lying; for "cutting a dyke" is just the thing that might preserve us from an "encroaching desert.") And the German philosopher Rudolph Eucken: "We have a right to say that we form the soul of humanity and that the destruction of German nature would rob world history of its deepest meaning." Quoted in ibid., p. 98. French thinkers claim likewise for France, identifying their war effort with Christ: "No doubt we are fighting for ourselves," said Karl Sabatier, "but we are fighting, too, for all peoples. The France of today is fighting religiously. . . . We all feel that our sorrows continue and fulfill those of the innocent victim of Calvary." Quoted in ibid., p. 98.

At the conclusion of the Spanish American War, Niebuhr writes, the fiction was created that the "fortunes of war had made us the unwilling recipients and custodians of the Philippine Islands." President McKinley ordered the commission negotiating a peace treaty with Spain to "be as scrupulous and magnanimous in the concluding settlement as the nation had been just and humane in the original action." But the greed for possessions was rising, and presently the President stiffened American demands, invoking God and additionally charging his commissioners to remember that "the march of events rules and overrules human action. We cannot be unmindful that without any design on our part the war has brought us new responsibilities and duties which we must meet and discharge as becomes a great nation on whose growth and career from the beginning the Ruler of Nations has plainly written the high command and pledge of civilization." When after a "great deal of negotiation among the commissioners," writes Niebuhr, "and much debate between imperialists and anti-imperialists in America it was finally decided to ask for all of the Philippines, Secretary Hay wrote to the commissioners: 'You are instructed to insist on the cession of the whole of the Philippines. . . . The questions of duty and humanity appeal to the President so strongly that he can find no appropriate answer but the one he has marked out.'" Sometime later President McKinley, speaking to a group of clergymen, explained how he arrived at this decision: "I walked the floor of the White House night after night until midnight; and I am not ashamed to tell you gentlemen that I went on my knees and prayed to Almighty God for light and guidance more than one night. And one night it came to me this way—that there was nothing left for us to do but to take them all, and to educate the Filipinos, and uplift and civilize and Christianize them, and by God's grace do the very best we could by them, as our fellowmen for whom Christ also died. And then I went to bed and went to sleep and slept soundly." Quoted in ibid., pp. 100–102.

Notes

Nathaniel Peffer offers a drier version: "Much might be said of their fitness for self-government, but why? What does it matter? The Filipinos will seize the government and proclaim themselves independent tomorrow if they had the power, and if when they have the power, they will, whether fit for self-government or not. And were they as politically wise as Solons, the American Government would not give them their independence now, nor a hundred years from now, if American interests were to lose thereby." Quoted in ibid., pp. 102–103.

2. Mumford (30), p. 14.

3. "Now evil on earth," according to Jacob Burckhardt, "is assuredly a part of the great economy of world history. It is force, the right of the stronger over the weaker, prefigured in that struggle for life which fills all nature, the animal and the vegetable worlds, and is carried on in the early stages of humanity by murder and robbery, by the eviction, extermination or enslavement of weaker races, or of weaker peoples within the same race, of weaker States, of weaker social classes within the same State and people." The Roman Empire, he points out, was inaugurated by the most frightful methods and was completed by the subjection of East and West in rivers of blood. It culminated nonetheless in a common world culture which made possible the spread of a world religion. "Yet from the fact that good came of evil, and relative happiness of misery, we cannot in any way deduce that evil and misery were not, at the outset, what they were. Every successful act of violence is evil, and at the very least a dangerous example. But when that act was the foundation of power, it was followed by the indefatigable efforts of men to turn mere power into law and order. With their healthy strength, they set to work to cure the State of violence." More ancient times, he says, "present a picture of horror when we imagine the sum of despair and misery which went to establish the old world Empires. . . . Our deepest compassion, perhaps, would go out to those individual peoples who must have succumbed to the Kings of Persia, or even to the Kings of Assyria and Media, in their desperate struggle for independence. All the lonely royal fortresses of individual peoples (Hyrcanians, Bactrians, Sogdanians, Gedrosians) which Alexander encountered marked the scenes of ghastly last struggles, of which all knowledge has been lost. Did they fight in vain? . . . One thing, however, must be said of all great destructions: since we cannot fathom the economy of world history, we never know what would have happened if some event, however terrible, had not occurred. Instead of one wave of history which we know, another, which we do not know, would have risen; instead of one evil oppressor, perhaps one still more evil. . . . It may be, too, that if those who succumbed had lived longer, they would no longer have seemed worthy of our compassion. A people . . . that succumbed early in the glorious struggle might later not have been very happy, not very civilized, early corrupted by its own iniquity and deadly to its neighbors. But, having perished in the flower of its

strength, we feel toward it as we feel toward exceptional men who have died young; we imagine that, had they lived, they could not but have progressed in good fortune and greatness, while perhaps their meridian already lay behind them. . . . Bloom and decay are certainly the common lot, but every really personal life that is cut off by violence, and (in our opinion) prematurely, must be regarded as absolutely irreplaceable, indeed as irreplaceable even by one of equal excellence." Burckhardt (9), pp. 361–366.

4. "Caesar and Napoleon," writes Karl Löwith, describing Hegel's view, "did not and could not know what they were doing when they consolidated their own positions. They fulfilled unknowingly a general purpose in the history of the Occident. The apparent freedom of their actions is the ambiguous freedom of passions pursuing, with an animal faith, a particular purpose, but in such a way that the pursuit of their individual interests is prompted and driven by an anonymous impulse, necessitating their will and decisions. The universal purpose and the particular intention meet in this dialectic of passionate action; for that which world-historical individuals are unconsciously driving at is not what they are consciously planning but what they *must* will, out of an urge which seems to be blind and yet has a wider perspective than personal interest." Löwith (25), p. 55.

"The discord," writes Hegel, describing the rise of Christianity, "between the inner life of the heart and the actual world is removed. All the sacrifices that have ever and anon been laid on the altar of the earth are justified for the sake of this ultimate purpose." Quoted in ibid., p. 57. And: "Just as the movement of the ocean prevents the corruption which would be the result of perpetual calm, so by war people escape the corruption which would be occasioned by a continuous or eternal peace." Quoted by Brinton (7), p. 336. Bertrand Russell notes that if such a philosophy of history is to be made plausible, it requires "some distortion of facts and considerable ignorance. Hegel, like Marx and Spengler after him, possessed both these qualifications. It is odd that a process which is represented as cosmic should have taken place on our planet, and most of it near the Mediterranean. Nor is there any reason, if reality is timeless, why the later parts of the process should embody higher categories than the earlier parts—unless one were to adopt the blasphemous supposition that the Universe was gradually learning Hegel's philosophy." Russell (38), p. 735.

VII
Jungle and Community

1. "As the wary Panzers drew back into the Arnswalde," writes Alan Clark, "they gathered up in their tracks a whole mass of civilian flot-

sam. Infants and aged, wounded, slave labourers . . . deserters in various disguises, crowded the roads and byways, huddled in broken carts, spawned over the bleak white-streaked countryside like maggots on an open wound. . . . Rape, pillage, and random destruction seethed on the crest of the advancing Russian wave. To Soviet soldiers killing was incidental; the very fecklessness with which they valued human life made its taking, or sparing, a trivial matter. In contrast, the German blood lust was a positive and accelerating cancer which, having devoured so many subject peoples, was now beginning fast to consume the *Herrenvolk* themselves. Men of the *Volkssturm*, hurrying up to the Oder, could see the bodies of 'malcontents,' their former comrades in arms, swinging from the twisted girders of the blown-up bridges, where they had been hanged by special flying courts-martial which ranged the military zone, pronouncing and executing sentence at will. Every tree in the Hindenburg Allee in Danzig had been used as a gibbet, and the dangling soldiers kicked and threshed, sometimes for hours, with placards pinned to their uniforms: 'I hang here because I left my unit without permission.' Many of the 'deserters' had been schoolboy flak gunners who had gone to visit their parents for a few hours, proud of the opportunity to display their new uniforms." Clark (14), pp. 482–483.

2. Ibid., p. 483.

3. Popper (34), p. 351. A revolution, he writes in another context, "always destroys the institutional and traditional framework of society. It must thereby endanger the very set of values for the realization of which it has been undertaken. Indeed, a set of values can have social significance only insofar as there exists a social tradition which upholds them. This is true of the aims of a revolution as much as of any other values." Ibid., p. 343.

VIII

Hierarchy

1. "Evil now comes about," writes Charles Reich, "not necessarily when people violate what they understand to be their duty but, more and more often, when they are conscientiously doing what is expected of them. And for this evil the question of individual blame seems almost irrelevant." For ages, he points out, we have believed the root of crime to be a guilty mind or a malign heart, and our procedures of justice have been designed to ferret out such criminal intent, to expose it and punish it. But for our modern evils no investigation, no technical fixing of blame, is likely to disclose a malign heart. "From wiretapping to the prosecution of the Vietnam war, our crimes have been started and carried out by men zealously attempting to serve as they have been taught to serve. . . . Evil today is the product of our system of organization

and our technology, and . . . it occurs because personal responsibility and personal awareness have been obliterated by a system deliberately designed to do just that—eliminate or minimize the human element and insure the supremacy of the system. . . . It is this rational organization of human effort that has brought us to our present stage of civilization, but we should realize that inherent in the very design of the system is the disappearance of individual blame, and hence the obsolescence of our concepts of individual criminal responsibility. . . . A scientist who is doing his specialized duty to further research and knowledge develops the substance known as napalm. Another specialist makes policy in the field of our nation's foreign affairs. A third is concerned with maintaining the strength of our armed forces with the most modern weaponry. A fourth manufactures what the defense authorities require. A fifth drops napalm from an airplane where he is told to do so. The ultimate evil is the result of carefully segmented acts; the structure itself guarantees an evasion by everyone of responsibility for the full moral act. Indeed, the system, especially when it is combined with advanced technology, makes it unlikely that those who participate in the process will have any real awareness of the ultimate consequences. Neither the scientist nor the man in the State Department nor even the pilot actually sees the horrors of burning napalm on human flesh. The basic result of our system of doing things is to destroy awareness, alienate all of us from the consequences of our actions, and prevent the formation of that very responsibility which has been at the center of our idea of criminal justice." Reich (37), pp. 52–57.

2. Russell (38), p. 744.

3. Ayres (1), pp. 92–93.

4. Ibid., p. 97.

5. The concept of hierarchy is a magic tool which seems to resolve any conflict. With its mastery comes a giddy intimation of intellectual omnipotence. Dilemmas of a lifetime fade away. It gives us depth perception, enables us suddenly to see that two values equally ultimate which appear to be in head-on conflict are rather like trains on adjacent tracks which go in opposite directions but do not collide. We feel elation, sense a secret promise. Could it be that all conflict between ultimate values is of this kind? that all irrefutable truths which strain against each other may be so explained? Perhaps all genuine values really are compatible, and in principle even if never in practice the perfect society could be built. So we come again to that major assumption of all Western thought, whether rationalist or empiricist, skeptical or dogmatic, that belief (to quote Isaiah Berlin) "that somewhere in the past or the future, in this world or the next, in the church or the laboratory, in the speculations of the metaphysician or the findings of the social scientist or in the uncorrupted heart of the simple good man, there is to be found the final solution of the question of how men should live. If this is false (and if more than one equally valid answer to

the question can be returned, then it is false) the idea of the sole true, objective, universal human ideal crumbles. The very search for it becomes not merely utopian in practice, but conceptually incoherent." Berlin (6), p. 31.

6. Cf. Koestler (20).

7. Ibid., p. 233. All italics in original.

8. Ibid., p. 238.

9. Ibid., pp. 241–242.

10. Ibid., p. 308.

11. Ibid., pp. 251, 253.

12. Niebuhr (31), p. 91.

13. "The trouble started with the sudden mushrooming of the neocortex at a rate 'unprecedented in evolutionary history'. . . . The lines of communication between the very old and the brand-new structures were not developed sufficiently to guarantee their harmonious interplay, the hierarchic co-ordination of instinct and intelligence." The neurophysiological evidence indicates, he says, a "dissonance between the reactions of neocortex and limbic system. Instead of functioning as integral parts in a hierarchic order, they lead a kind of agonized coexistence." He believes it possible—and soon—that by the mass use of new drugs we will achieve "an artificially simulated, adaptive mutation to bridge the rift between phylogenetically old and new brain, between instinct and intellect, emotion and reason. If it is within our reach to increase man's suggestibility, it will be soon within our reach to do the opposite, to counteract misplaced devotion and that militant enthusiasm, both murderous and suicidal, which we see reflected in the pages of the daily newspaper. The most urgent task of biochemistry is the search for a remedy. . . . It is not Utopian to believe that it can and will be done." Koestler (20), pp. 331, 332, 336.

IX

The Meta-Conscious

1. While we are often "not aware," he continues, "of mental processes because they have not risen to the level of consciousness but proceed on what are (both physiologically and psychologically) lower levels, there is no reason why the conscious level should be the highest level, and there are many grounds which make it probable that, in order to be conscious, processes must be guided by a supra-conscious order which cannot be the object of its own representations. Mental events may thus be unconscious and uncommunicable because they proceed on too high a level as well as because they proceed on too low a level. To put this differently: if 'to have meaning' is to have a place in an order which we share with other people, this order itself cannot

have meaning because it cannot have a place in itself. . . . There will always be some rules governing a mind which that mind in its then prevailing state cannot communicate, and . . . if it ever were to acquire the capacity of communicating these rules, this would presuppose that it had acquired further higher rules which make the communication of the former possible but which themselves would still be incommunicable. . . . All we can talk about and probably all we can consciously think about presupposes the existence of a framework which determines its meaning, i.e., a system of rules which operate us but which we can neither state nor form an image of and which we can merely evoke in others insofar as they already possess them." Hayek (19), pp. 61–62.

2. "The barriers had fallen once more," writes Isaiah Berlin, "this time it seemed forever. The king had fled, declaring that 'he had been driven out by moral forces,' a new Government had been appointed containing representatives of all the friends of humanity and progress: the great physicist Arago and the poet Lamartine received portfolios, the workers were represented by Louis Blanc and Albert. Lamartine composed an eloquent manifesto which was read, quoted, declaimed everywhere. The streets were filled with an immense singing, cheering throng of democrats of all hues and nationalities. . . . News presently arrived that Naples had revolted; and after it Milan, Rome, Venice and other Italian cities. Berlin, Vienna, and Budapest had risen in arms. Europe was ablaze. . . ." It didn't last. Within a few months "the heroic phase of the Paris revolution had spent itself, and the conservative forces began to rally their strength. The socialist and radical members of the Government, Louis Blanc, Albert, Flocon, were forced to resign. The workers rebelled against the right-wing republicans who remained in power, threw up barricades, and after three days' hand-to-hand fighting in the streets, were dispersed and routed by the National Guard and troops which remained loyal to the Government." Berlin (5), pp. 169–170, 175.

3. Quoted in ibid., p. 159.

4. "As science learns one answer," writes Warren Weaver, "it is characteristically true that it also learns several new questions. It is as though science were working in a great forest of ignorance, making an ever larger circular clearing within which, not to insist on the pun, things are clear. . . . But, as that circle becomes larger and larger, the circumference of contact with ignorance also gets longer and longer. Science learns more and more. But there is an ultimate sense in which it does not gain; for the volume of the appreciated but not understood keeps getting larger. We keep, in science, getting a more and more sophisticated view of our ignorance." "A Scientist Ponders Faith," *Saturday Review*, January 3, 1959. Quoted in Hayek (19), p. 40.

5. Most of the advantages of social life," writes Hayek, ". . . rest on the fact that the individual benefits from more knowledge than he is aware of. It might be said that civilization begins when the individual in

the pursuit of his ends can make use of more knowledge than he has himself acquired and when he can transcend the boundaries of his ignorance by profiting from knowledge he does not himself possess." Hayek (18), p. 22. According to Alfred North Whitehead, "Civilization advances by extending the number of important operations which we can perform without thinking about them. Operations of thought are like cavalry charges in a battle—they are strictly limited in number, they require fresh horses, and must only be made at decisive moments." Quoted by Hayek (18), p. 22.

6. "While the growth of our knowledge of nature constantly discloses new realms of ignorance, the increasing complexity of the civilization which this knowledge enables us to build presents new obstacles to the intellectual comprehension of the world around us. The more men know, the smaller the share of all that knowledge becomes that any one mind can absorb. The more civilized we become, the more relatively ignorant must each individual be of the facts on which the working of his civilization depends." Hayek (18), p. 26.

7. "Now as regards the opinions of the saints about these matters of nature," wrote the seventeenth-century astronomer Johannes Kepler, "I answer in one word, that in theology the weight of Authority, but in philosophy the weight of Reason alone is valid. Therefore a saint was Lanctantius, who denied the earth's rotundity; a saint was Augustine who admitted the rotundity, but denied that antipodes exist. Sacred is the Holy Office of our day, which admits the smallness of the earth but denies its motion: but to me more sacred than all these is Truth, when I, with all respect for the doctors of the Church, demonstrate from philosophy that the earth is round, circumhabited by antipodes, of a most insignificant smallness, and a swift wanderer among the stars." Quoted in Koestler (21), p. 343. And Galileo: "Methinks that in the discussion of natural problems we ought not to begin at the authority of places of Scripture, but at sensible experiments and necessary illustrations. . . . Nature, being inexorable and immutable, and never passing the bounds of the laws assigned her . . . I conceive that, concerning natural effects, that which either sensible experience sets before our eyes, or necessary demonstrations do prove unto us, ought not, on any account, to be called into question, much less condemned upon the testimony of texts of Scripture, which may, under their words, couch senses seemingly contrary thereto." Quoted in Bronowski and Mazlish (8), p. 125.

8. Quoted in Koestler (21), pp. 393–394.

9. And if the state may do as it will, why may not the individual? "I do not demand any right," said the anarchist philosopher Max Stirner, "therefore I need not recognize any either. What I can get by force I get by force, and what I do not get by force I have no right to, nor do I give myself airs or consolation, with my imprescriptible right. . . . What then is *my* property? Nothing but what is in my power! To what property am I entitled? To every property to which I—

empower myself. I give myself the right of property in taking property to myself, or giving myself the proprietor's power. . . . Let me then withdraw the might that I have conceded to others out of ignorance regarding the strength of my own might! Let me say to myself, what my might reaches to is my property; and let me claim as property everything that I feel myself strong enough to attain, and let me extend my actual property as far as *I* entitle, that is, empower, myself to take." Quoted in Krimerman and Perry (22), pp. 176, 179.

If I forego something I want and can have, it can only be because someone else's compunction has slipped unnoticed into my conscience. And why honor that? Why not institute individually my own age of rebellion, cast out the alien prohibition and do as I will? Murder becomes legal, crime assumes the garb of reason, and it is innocence itself, Camus points out, that is called upon to justify itself. The victorious revolt of man's reason against God's authority has abandoned us in a contradiction, "with no grounds either for preventing or for justifying murder, menacing and menaced, swept along with a whole generation intoxicated by nihilism, and yet lost in loneliness, with weapons in our hands and a lump in our throats." Camus (11), p. 8.

10. Camus (11), p. 10.
11. Berlin (4), pp. 165–166.
12. Hayek (19), p. 165.
13. Ibid.
14. Ibid.
15. Popper (34), p. 350. Italics in original.
16. Hayek (19), pp. 165–166.
17. Ibid., p. 170.

X

Progress

1. Westermarck (43), II., 746.
2. "Historical Christianity," writes Camus, "postpones to a point beyond the span of history the cure of evil and murder, which are nevertheless experienced within the span of history. Contemporary materialism also believes that it can answer all questions. But, as a slave to history, it increases the domain of historic murder and at the same time leaves it without any justification, except in the future—which again demands faith. In both cases one must wait, and meanwhile the innocent continue to die. For twenty centuries the sum total of evil has not diminished in the world. No paradise, whether divine or revolutionary, has been realized." Camus (11), p. 303.
3. Thucydides (41), p. 337.
4. Brinton (7), p. 421.

Notes

5. The order, writes Hayek, "which has progressively grown beyond the organizations of the family, the horde, the clan and the tribe, the principalities and even the empire or national state, and has produced at least the beginning of a world society, is based on the adoption—without and often against the desire of political authority—of rules which came to prevail because the groups who observed them were more successful; and it has existed and grown in extent long before people were aware of its existence or understood its operation." Hayek (19), pp. 163–164.

6. "I was returning to the Left Bank and my home by way of the Pont Royal," says Jean-Baptiste Clamence in Camus' *The Fall.* "It was an hour past midnight, a fine rain was falling, a drizzle rather, that scattered the few people on the streets. I had just left a mistress, who was surely already asleep. I was enjoying that walk, a little numbed, my body calmed and irrigated by a flow of blood gentle as the falling rain. On the bridge I passed behind a figure leaning over the railing and seeming to stare at the river. On closer view, I made out a slim young woman dressed in black. The back of her neck, cool and damp between her dark hair and coat collar, stirred me. But I went on after a moment's hesitation. At the end of the bridge I followed the quays toward Saint-Michel, where I lived. I had already gone some fifty yards when I heard the sound—which, despite the distance, seemed dreadfully loud in the midnight silence—of a body striking the water. I stopped short, but without turning around. Almost at once I heard a cry, repeated several times, which was going downstream; then it suddenly ceased. The silence that followed, as the night suddenly stood still, seemed interminable. I wanted to run and yet didn't stir. I was trembling, I believe from cold and shock. I told myself that I had to be quick and I felt an irresistible weakness steal over me. I have forgotten what I thought then. 'Too late, too far . . .' or something of the sort. I was listening as I stood motionless. Then, slowly under the rain, I went away. I informed no one." Camus (10), pp. 69–70.

7. "Life propagates itself," writes Teilhard de Chardin, "by ceaselessly adding to itself what it successively acquires—like memory. . . . Every living being passes on to his successor the being he himself inherited, not merely diversified but accentuated in a given direction, according to the line to which he belongs. And all the lines, whatever their nature, seem in varying degrees and each after its own formula to move a greater or lesser distance in the general direction of greater spontaneity and consciousness. Something passes, something goes, through the long chain of living creatures." Teilhard de Chardin (40), p. 25.

WORKS CITED

1. AYRES, C. E. *The Theory of Economic Progress.* Chapel Hill, N.C.: The University of North Carolina Press, 1944.

2. BAY, Christian. *The Structure of Freedom.* Stanford, California: Stanford University Press, 1958.

3. BECKER, Carl L. *The Heavenly City of the Eighteenth-Century Philosophers.* New Haven: Yale University Press, 1932.

4. BERLIN, Isaiah. *Four Essays on Liberty.* New York: Oxford University Press, 1969.

5. ———. *Karl Marx: His Life and Environment.* New York: Oxford University Press, 1970. (First edition published in 1939 in the Home University Library.)

6. ———. "The Question of Machiavelli," *The New York Review of Books,* XVII, No. 7 (November 4, 1971), 20–32.

7. BRINTON, Crane. *A History of Western Morals.* New York: Harcourt Brace Jovanovich, 1959.

8. BRONOWSKI, J., and MAZLISH, Bruce. *The Western Intellectual Tradition: From Leonardo to Hegel.* London: Hutchinson & Co., Ltd., 1960.

9. BURCKHARDT, Jacob. *Force and Freedom: Reflections on History.* Edited by James Hastings Nichols. New York: Pantheon Books, 1943.

10. CAMUS, Albert. *The Fall.* Translated by Justin O'Brien. New York: Alfred A. Knopf, Inc., 1956.

11. ———. *The Rebel: An Essay on Man in Revolt.* Translated by Anthony Bower. New York: Vintage Books, 1956.

12. ———. *Resistance, Rebellion, and Death.* Translated by Justin O'Brien. New York: Alfred A. Knopf, Inc., 1961.

13. CARR, E. H. *Michael Bakunin.* New York: Vintage Books, n.d. (First published by Macmillan and Co., 1937.)

14. CLARK, Alan. *Barbarossa: The Russian-German Conflict, 1941–45.* New York: The New American Library, Inc., 1965.

15. DOSTOYEVSKY, Fyodor. *The Brothers Karamazov.* Translated by Constance Garnett. New York: Random House, 1933.

157

16. FLETCHER, Joseph. *Situation Ethics*. Philadelphia: The Westminster Press, 1966.

17. GERTH, H. H., and MILLS, C. Wright, eds. *From Max Weber: Essays in Sociology*. New York: Oxford University Press, 1946.

18. HAYEK, F. A. *The Constitution of Liberty*. Chicago: The University of Chicago Press, 1960.

19. ———. *Studies in Philosophy, Politics and Economics*. New York: Simon & Schuster, 1967.

20. KOESTLER, Arthur. *The Ghost in the Machine*. London: Hutchinson & Co., Ltd., 1967.

21. ———. *The Sleepwalkers*. New York: Grosset & Dunlap, 1963.

22. KRIMERMAN, Leonard I., and PERRY, Lewis, eds. *Patterns of Anarchy: A Collection of Writings on the Anarchist Tradition*. Garden City, N.Y.: Doubleday & Co., Inc., 1966.

23. LECKY, W. E. H. *History of European Morals From Augustus to Charlemagne*. New York: George Braziller, 1955. (Original edition: London, 1869.)

24. ———. *History of the Rise and Influence of the Spirit of Rationalism in Europe*. 2 vols. London: Longmans, Green, and Co., 1866.

25. LÖWITH, Karl. *Meaning in History*. Chicago: The University of Chicago Press, 1937.

26. McLUHAN, Marshall. *Understanding Media: The Extensions of Man*. New York: McGraw-Hill Book Co., 1964.

27. MEYERHOFF, Hans. *The Philosophy of History in Our Time: An Anthology*. Garden City, N. Y.: Doubleday & Co., Inc., 1959.

28. MILL, John Stuart. *Utilitarianism, Liberty, and Representative Government*. London: J. M. Dent and Sons, Ltd. n.d.

29. MITCHELL, Edwin T. *A System of Ethics*. New York: Charles Scribner's Sons, 1950.

30. MUMFORD, Lewis. *Art and Technics*. New York: Columbia University Press, 1952.

31. NIEBUHR, Reinhold. *Moral Man and Immoral Society*. New York: Charles Scribner's Sons, 1932.

32. PETERS, H. F. *My Sister, My Spouse: A Biography of Lou Andreas-Salome*. New York: W. W. Norton & Co., Inc., 1962.

33. PLUMB, J. H. *The Death of the Past*. Boston: Houghton Mifflin Company, 1970.

34. POPPER, Karl R. *Conjectures and Refutation*. New York: Basic Books, Publishers, 1962.

35. ———. *The Open Society and Its Enemies*. Princeton, N.J.: Princeton University Press, 1950.

36. PRESCOTT, William H. *History of the Conquest of Mexico*. 2 vols. bound as one. New York: A. L. Burt Company, 1843.

37. REICH, Charles A. "Reflections: The Limits of Duty," *The New Yorker*, June 19, 1971, pp. 52–57.

Works Cited

38. RUSSELL, Bertrand. *A History of Western Philosophy*. New York: Simon & Schuster, 1945.

39. SCHLESINGER, Arthur Jr. "The Necessary Amorality of Foreign Affairs," *Harper's*, August 1971, pp. 72–77.

40. TEILHARD de CHARDIN, Pierre. *The Future of Man*. Translated by Norman Denny. New York: Harper & Row, Publishers, 1964.

41. THUCYDIDES. *The Peloponnesian War*. New York: Random House, Inc., 1951.

42. TRILLING, Lionel. *Sincerity and Authenticity*. Cambridge, Mass.: Harvard University Press, 1972.

43. WESTERMARCK, Edward. *The Origin and Development of the Moral Ideas*. 2 vols. New York: The Macmillan Co., 1906–1908.

INDEX

Index

Index

Index